SMILE THERAPY

OPTIMA

SMILE THERAPY

LIZ HODGKINSON

ILLUSTRATED BY CHRIS WINN

An OPTIMA book

First published in 1987 by
Macdonald Optima, a division of
Macdonald & Co. (Publishers) Ltd

A BPCC PLC company

British Library Cataloguing in Publication Data

Hodgkinson, Liz
    Smile therapy.
    1. Laugher —— Therapeutic use
    2. Smile —— Therapeutic use
    I. Title
    615.8′51   RC489.H85

    ISBN 0-356-12790-7

Macdonald & Co. (Publishers) Ltd
3rd Floor
Greater London House
Hampstead Road
London NW1 7QX

Printed in Great Britain by
The Guernsey Press Co. Ltd.
Guernsey, Channel Islands

For Theo Richmond,
who always makes me smile.

CONTENTS

INTRODUCTION

In *The Happy Hypocrite*, a short story by Max Beerhohm, a vicious, evil man named Lord George Hell suddenly falls in love with a beautiful young girl. Unfortunately for him, she has said she will only ever love somebody who has the face of a saint, and Lord George's resembles that of the devil. In desperation, because he has decided he cannot live without the love of this lady, Lord George buys an angelic-looking mask from a mask maker. He has it stuck on so that it can never come off, and so that his young lover will never know about the evil visage below.

He presents himself to his love while wearing the mask and she instantly falls in love with him. The blissful pair get married and live happily ever after in an idyllic country cottage. One day, however, a former lady love of Lord George's turns up in a fury. She has recognized him for who he really is. She tears off his mask to expose the evil face beneath, and Lord George fears that all is lost. But, while wearing the mask of a saint, Lord George's own face has been undergoing a dramatic transformation. It has become exactly like the mask — so he no longer needs to wear it anyway.

By pretending to be saintly, and wearing the mask of a saint, Lord George has become good, through and through. Max Beerbohm's story is, of course, purely a fantasy, and not based on any scientific investigation or research about how facial expressions can affect personality. But the story has stood the test of time, and for a simple reason — it is true.

This book has been written in the belief that facial expressions do intimately affect personality, and states of mind. If we cultivate an expressin of serenity, we will ultimately become serene. If we keep smiling, we will eventually become happy. Conversely, if we look miserable and downcast all the time, we shall soon become miserable inside.

THE SCIENTIFIC EVIDENCE

Perhaps at first the idea that our facial expressions can actually affect the way we feel and act sounds far-fetched, like Max Beerbohm's story. But actually, there is now a great deal of scientific evidence to back it up.

Much of the evidence is not even all that new. The theory was first put forward at the turn of the century by a French physiologist called Israel Waynbaum. He was certain that when facial muscles are moved, hormonal mechanisms in the brain are activated. The different facial muscles that are used for smiling, showing anger, disgust and so on, all connect to different neurotransmitters in the brain. These send chemical messages throughout the body. Smiling, believed Waynbaum, affects these hormones positively, whereas all other expressions have a negative effect.

Waynbaum wrote a book explaining his theory, but it had lain forgotten for many years. Recently though, the idea was revived in America and put to the test by a group of American scientists. They soon discovered that there was truth in the hypothesis: facial expressions really do have a profound effect on the way we think and feel.

In one experiment, a group of actors was asked to simulate a range of facial expressions which were associated with various emotions. They were asked to look in turn happy, sad, disgusted and surprised. As each expression flitted over the face, instruments recorded any changes in heart rate, skin temperature and blood pressure.

It was found that far-reaching physiological changes accompanied each facial expression. For most of the emotions simulated, all body systems were hyped up. When the subjects began to smile, however, heart rate decreased, blood pressure went down and the body systems were relaxed. With smiling, all changes were beneficial, whereas for the other expressions the body changes were negative. It has to be remembered that, throughout this experiment, the subjects were not actually *feeling* happy, sad or disgusted, but were merely contorting their facial muscles into the expressions associated with these emotions.

The results of this and other experiments have shown that smiling and laughter, far from being empty, vaguely enjoyable social gestures, actually have a profound part to play in the maintenance of health and the avoidance of illness. If we keep smiling, even when we feel miserable inside, we help our body systems to stay calm and relaxed. The main function of smiling and laughter, it seems, is to reduce stress and tension, the 20th-century's biggest health destroyers.

LAUGHTER AS MEDICINE

It has been said for centuries that laughter is the best medicine, but in recent years we have not given this idea very much credence. Doctors have preferred to use pills, surgery and other invasive methods to treat illness. They

13

would probably laugh themselves at any suggestion that smiling might be more efficacious. The possibility that you could smile yourself better seems ludicrous to those who have spent seven years learning medicine. Isn't illness a very serious business, and no laughing matter? When people are ill, they hardly feel much like laughing, and hearty laughter would seem to be extremely inappropriate in a hospital ward.

That certainly used to be the prevailing belief. But now doctors are starting to discover for themselves that smiling and laughter actually help people to get better in hospital, whereas glum faces can be a factor in prolonging illness.

The reason for this is that when people smile and laugh, it shows they are not afraid. It is actually impossible to laugh and feel fear at the same time, as the one activity automatically drives out the other. We laugh when we feel relaxed and at ease. It is now increasingly being accepted that much of illness develops from feelings of fear. All undue stress is caused by fear, and this stress in time sets up imbalances in the body which can lead to a breakdown.

When stress hormones are permanently being produced in excess quantities, the immune system cannot work properly, and the way is opened up for all kinds of infections to come in, and internal organs to be put under severe strain. Smiling and laughter can be potent weapons to attack the vicious cycle of fear and stress, and can stop them building up to dangerous levels.

We know now that happy people get ill less often than those who are chronically miserable and anxious. Those who can see the bright side of life and remain optismistic are unlikely to go down with stress-related disorders.Those who deliberately smile whenever possible are helping themselves to stay relaxed and calm.

The therapeutic value of smiling does not just lie with the person who smiles, however. There is an infectious element to smiling and laughter, and one smiling person can actually change the mood of those around. People who smile a lot are not just keeping themselves well, but helping others to get better too. Human beings are very

imitative creatures, and we easily pick up the moods of other people, whether these are positive or negative.

How often have you felt yourself affected by the atmosphere in a room? People waiting together for the results of an examination or important competition can sense an almost tangible tension. We hear phrases like: 'The atmosphere was so thick you could cut it with a knife.' Just as anxiety and tension can make an atmosphere seem heavy, so smiling and laughter can lighten it. And any lightening of stress or tension must inevitably make people feel better inside.

Very many people develop illnesses because they take themselves and the world around them far too seriously. In some cases, people actually become afraid to laugh, in case it makes them seem frivolous or unintelligent. People are also afraid of being laughed at. Yet, if you think about it, smiling and laughing are actually among the most intelligent things you can do. Human beings are the only creatures who can smile, laugh and see a joke — and we ought to be making more of this capacity.

The ability to laugh, more than almost anything else, is what distinguishes humans from other animals. Animals can feel stress, they can be anxious and miserable, they can be terrified — but they can't laugh out loud. It appears that laughter is, above all, a safety mechanism given to humans to enable them to stay well and happy.

All the evidence we have available now shows that humans are meant to be happy, laughing creatures, rather than sad and miserable individuals. The very first 'human' expression a baby has is that of smiling. The very first separate emotion a baby feels is that of happiness. Of course, babies do cry, as soon as they are born, but that comes from generalized distress rather than a separate response to a given stimulus. It is also at first the only sound they can make. Infants do not show grief, anger, sadness or misery on their faces until long after they have learned to laugh and smile. It seems from this that the capacity for laughter and happiness are innate, whereas the other, negative emotions are learned behaviour which comes later.

People can and have cured themselves from serious illness simply by making themselves laugh. The most famous example is that of Norman Cousins, whose case is described later in the book. He baffled doctors when he got better from a supposedly incurable illness by hiring films that made him laugh. Cousins' theory, which he put into practice, was that, just as negative emotions can make us ill, so positive emotions must be able to make us well again. For years, doctors poured scorn on Cousins' idea and dismissed his thesis, but now at last, researchers all over the world are investigating the therapeutic benefits of smiling and laughing. Several French neurologists have investigated what happens to the body during a bout of laughter. They have come to the conclusion that laughter does only good. There are no adverse side effects, the therapy is cheap, and it is something everyone can do unaided.

The act of laughter can set in motion far-reaching physiological changes such as improving digestion, relaxing and stabilizing all body systems and improving circulation.

Though an ever-increasing body of medical opinion now suggests that laughter can be a potent healing tool, on the whole hospitals and doctors in surgeries have been slow to accept it. Surgeries and hospitals are not places people visit for fun. They are not conducive to laughter. A hundred years ago, hospitals were a health risk in themselves. Now that we have largely conquered the problem of hygiene, it is time to pay attention to the atmosphere in hospitals. People are afraid of them, and this fear is embedded in the very walls. Even visitors feel anxious in hospitals. Yet if they were made jollier places, doctors would find that the tension lifted, and patients improved more quickly.

THE PSYCHOLOGY OF SMILING

The psychology of smiling is still in its infancy, but we know enough to realize it has a fundamental importance in our lives. People should feel they have a duty, both to themselves and others, to smile and look cheerful rather than sad and downcast. This book contains a plea for everybody — ordinary men and women, politicians, doctors, nurses, and others in authority, to rediscover in themselves the laughter principle. Smiling and laughter have no adverse side effects at all. Even if large doses of laughter cannot by themselves cure every illness, they would at least allow some respite from the worry and pain that illness brings. Laughter is the best tranquillizer in the world.

Of course, smiling has many benefits other than the reversal of illness and maintenance of health. Smiles and laughter are the best ice-breakers at social gatherings. When people can laugh together, they cease to be nervous of each other. Laughter casts out feelings of hostility which are often present when strangers meet. Smiles oil the wheels of social life and make all gatherings infinitely more enjoyable. Smiles offer friendship. When people like each other, they smile. It's not too much to suggest that serious summit conferences between major political powers would be more constructive if world leaders could learn to smile at each other more, instead of looking grim.

People are often afraid that if they laugh and smile too much, others won't take them seriously. But the biggest problem with the world today is too little laughter rather than too much. A survey published in a French newspaper showed that people smile far less, on average, than they did 50 years ago. Laughter and humour are qualities that make the world go round. A sense of humour is, above all, the ability to laugh at yourself before anybody else does. No wonder it is the quality women prize most in a man — a man who has a well-developed sense of humour cannot possibly be a monster.

Very often, when people present an ever-unsmiling face to the world at large, it is because basically they are afraid. They cover up inner nervousness and shyness with an inscrutable, over-serious expression. Shyness, essentially, is withholding, whereas to smile and laugh shows a giving, outgoing and warmhearted personality.

Though we associate smiling and laughter with frivolity, far from frivolous changes occur in the brain and body when we smile, and physically express happiness. The whole body becomes tuned up and the brain becomes clearer.

The ability to smile readily is also of course a potent

beauty treatment. When people smile only one major muscle is used — whereas lots of muscles are needed to twist the face into expressions of grief or anger. Smiles keep people looking younger, whereas all the other facial expressions are ageing. Smiling is the best elixir of youth we have — and one that is within reach of us all.

Smiling makes people look more attractive, vital and youthful. There is everything to recommend it and nothing to say against it. Smiling can take a lot of the stress out of any situation, and actually make you feel happier inside.

Smile therapy is not pie in the sky — it's real.

1.
WHAT IS SMILING?

All over the world, human beings smile when they are happy. Anthropologists have observed that smiling is, in fact, the most universally recognizable of all human emotions. At a distance of 45 metres it is possible, apparently, to recognize a smile on somebody's face — but not any other emotion. You would have to get far closer to see whether the other person was registering surprise, anger, fear, disgust or shame.

The ability to smile also constitutes one of the main physiological differences between humans and animals. Though we may speak symbolically of the 'smile on the face of the tiger', we know that most animals cannot smile. When they bare their teeth they are usually neither happy nor smiling, but preparing to attack. Animals do not chuckle for the sheer joy of living. They do not really smile in greeting, nor laugh to relieve tension. The whole laughing mechanism is absent from the animal kingdom.

But as biologists and chemists know, we are biochemically extremely close to many animals, especially primates. Why is it, then, that we can laugh and they can't? Is the human ability to smile and laugh descended from any kind of animal gesture? Scientists have been asking themselves these questions for many hundreds of years, and several theories have evolved.

Since all humans are blessed with the ability to smile, they have argued, there must be some purpose in it all. So what is smiling, and what function does it serve?

Though these questions have been bothering scientists for so many years, we are only just now beginning to get a

glimpse of the answers. Humans have, very probably, been smiling at each other since the beginning of time, but it is only in the past 20 years or so that the phenomenon of smiling has been subjected to genuine scientific investigation. We still don't know everything about the dynamics of the smile, but we do know that it is supremely important for both social interaction and good health. We now know that people who smile readily are far more likely to remain physically and mentally healthy than those who perpetually look sad. We also know that smiling actually affects the production of certain hormones, and has a direct influence on heart rate and blood pressure.

A number of scientists working in the USA have come to the conclusion that smiling can be a potent healer, and can have a far more beneficial effect on serious illnesses than many modern drugs. Indeed, there are people who claim to have healed themselves from terminal conditions mainly by smiling and laughing. Though conventional doctors pour scorn on these accounts, there is no doubt that the people who tried this unusual method of healing did get better — and you can't argue with that.

HOW DID HUMANS LEARN TO SMILE?

According to Dr Paul Ekman, of the University of California, America's foremost researcher in this field, smiling is one of the simplest, most easily recognized yet at the same time one of the most confusing of human expressions. Only one facial muscle need be involved to produce a smile. This is the zygomatic major muscle, which reaches down from the cheekbone to the lip corners. By contrast, in order to look sad or disgusted, you would need to use at least two muscles to contort your visage into the appropriate grimace. The more angry or distressed your expression becomes, the more muscles are called into play. So, smiling is the easiest facial expression to assume. It is, if you like, the most natural one for humans to adopt.

Though Charles Darwin agonized long and hard over the possible evolutionary antecedents of the smile, he could not come to any kind of satisfactory conclusion about it. In the end, he had to admit that it had him baffled. All he and other later anthropologists could suggest was that the human smile might have originated from the 'threat display' in primates, where they bare their teeth to show anger or aggression. Perhaps smiling was a sign of dominant behaviour. It showed others that you were on top, and that they were less important.

But new knowledge about the science of smiling suggests that this traditional view cannot possibly be right. After all, babies smile when they are only a few weeks old. Can they possibly be exhibiting dominant behaviour? Lovers smile at each other, as do close relatives. But one is not necessarily being dominant over the other. It seems, rather, that those most dominant in our society are those who smile the least — politicians, lawyers, doctors and others in authority. We do not often see pictures of Adolf Hitler, for example, smiling happily. Also, it is known that women smile far more than men. Usually, female smiles do not indicate dominant behaviour.

There seems little substance in the traditional theory, and recent experiments with smiling and other human expressions suggest that it is completely invalid. When people are angry or aggressive, they produce more adrenaline, which charges the body and alerts the mind, ready for action. But when people smile, all their internal systems become relaxed.

This had now been shown conclusively in a series of experiments undertaken recently in America. In the experiments, a group of actors were asked to simulate a variety of emotions by putting the appropriate expression on their faces. They were asked to smile, to look surprised, angry, disgusted, fearful and sad. As they put on each expression in turn, various body functions, such as heart rate, skin temperature and blood pressure were monitored. In every case, smiling was the only expression which served to calm down the body's activity. All the other expressions, which indicated negative emotions, sent heart rate and blood pressure soaring.

Since these experiments have indicated that smiling is the only expression which actually lowers production of adrenaline and other arousal hormones, it is unlikely that it would have evolved from animal threat display, which is essentially aggressive and arousing.

An American primatologist, William B. Redican, offers a different and, to my mind, far more convincing explanation of the possible origin of human smiling. He asks the question: does an apparently similar expression in humans and animals necessarily signify a common motive? When animals bare their teeth and humans smile, are we talking about related activities? He believes the answer is no. We can, says Redican, spend much time describing the similar facial musculature of humans and apes, and the similarity of their nervous pathways, arousal hormones and the like, without getting anywhere near the root of the matter. Apes and gorillas, however intelligent they may be in relation to certain other animals, are basically simple creatures, whereas humans are infinitely complicated. Apes have a few set and predictable reactions to certain stimuli, whereas humans do not.

There is no logical reason to assume, says Redican, that because apes bare their teeth when preparing to attack, we humans are symbolically attacking someone or something every time we smile. We smile at a joke — is that a threat? We smile when we see kittens at play — is that a threat? An anthropologist would have to come up with some extremely clever arguments to be convincing here. There may, it is true, be some instances where certain types of smiling — the leer, or the grimace — may be interpreted as some kind of threat or aggressive behaviour. But, as we shall see later, those expressions are not really genuine forms of smiling.

William Redican defines the primates' threat display as a compound of aggression and fear. As the facial expression of threat grows more elaborate, the features become more mobile and hence more frightening to potential predators. The static gaping mouth, adds Redican, is a feature of facial displays in many animals, and it always indicates some kind of hostility. The more an animal engages in bared-teeth threat behaviour, the more dominant it is likely to be among its own kind. We do not, on the whole, regard smiling humans as threatening. Rather the opposite, in fact — they are seen as friendly. Usually, to smile at somebody means you are emphatically not hostile to them.

THE GRIMACE

Primates have a variation on the smile-type expression, usually known as the grimace, which is characterized by exposing the teeth prominently as the corners of the mouth and lips are retracted. In this display, the ears may be flattened, brows raised and the head drawn back on the shoulder. The primary emotion associated with the grimace is fear — an emotion which, like aggression, causes extra arousal in the body.

In primates, the grimace is associated with gaze aversion. When terrified, the animal will turn its head away so as not to see what dangers may be looming up. It is the classic reaction of the ostrich with its head in the sand. Again, it does not seem to have very much in common with human smiling, which is usually associated with eye contact, rather than turning the head away. When we meet a friend or lover, we tend to look at them rather than turning away.

Redican states that, although animals avert their gaze when they are trying to prevent an attack, they lock eyes with each other when a fight is actually going to take place. Their eyeball-to-eyeball contact is another sign of aggression. It is rarely so with humans. The mother who looks into her baby's eyes is not feeling hostile or aggressive, and is not about to attack her child. Usually, to look into someone's eyes is a sign of friendship, love and acceptance. We engage in eye contact when we are not afraid of the other person, when we want to come closer to them, establish a more intimate relationship.

When humans grimace, they are not smiling, nor are they usually feeling pleasure. Just the opposite in fact — a grimace is the expression of an unpleasant feeling. Redican says that while the human grimace and the primate grimace may have much in common, in that they are both associated with unpleasant events, the ape grimace cannot be a forerunner of the human smile. Humans grimace when they are, in Redican's words, 'anticipating a noxious or frightening event'. The grimace is, above all, in both humans and animals, an expression of fear.

Smiling also differs from grimacing because completely different sets of muscles are used to display the two expressions. When humans smile, they are using the zygomatic muscle, but when they pull a grimace, they use two others, the risorius and the platysma muscles. These have the effect of drawing the jaw downwards. The zygomatic muscle, by contrast makes the corners of the mouth draw backwards and upwards.

When we are frightened, we may grimace, but we do not smile. We may grimace on learning that we have lost a large sum of money, or that we have to undergo expensive, painful root canal treatment at the dentist's. But we are unliekly to smile.

THE PLAY FACE

So, concludes Redican, the assumed link between an animal grimace and a human smile has not been demonstrated anatomically. In his view, the human smile is far more likely to have originated from the so-called 'play face' of apes. This, he says, does bear a superficial resemblance to the threat display, but there are marked differences. The components of the play face in primates are that the mouth is wide open and the mouth corners are retracted only slightly. The upper lip may be tensed and curled over the upper incisors, but the teeth are not usually prominently displayed. This expression is associated with characteristic soft, grunting noises which are thought to be the precursor of human laughter. Redican says that there are many structural and muscular differences between the play face and the threat display, of which the most noticeable is the 'free and easy nature of eye and body movements'.

When an animal is putting on its play face, it is not afraid, it is not defending its territory but is actually enjoying itself. It feels confident and content. It is, suggests Redican, a far more likely precursor of the human smile than any facial behaviour associated with aggression, hostility or fear. A human smile is, above all, he argues, a play face. It shows that we are happy, and feel at ease. We do not, of course, know how far an animal may be consciously 'happy', but at least we know that when an animal is playing, it is feeling secure and not under threat.

It seems that smiling is intimately associated in humans with feelings of security and comfort. When we are afraid, tense, unhappy, startled or disgusted we feel, more than anything else, insecure. When we are afraid, it's because we don't know what is going to happen next, and worry that it may be unpleasant. We become apprehensive, and apprehension causes locked, rigid expressions which have nothing to do with the free and easy nature of a smile.

Psychologist Silvan Tomkins, who has researched extensively into the nature and origin of smiling, suggests that humans smile when there has been a sharp reduction of excessive stimulation and arousal. The smile of joy, he says, happens mainly 'when there is a sudden relief from negative stimulations such as pain, fear, distress, aggression'. Once these have gone, there is likely to be a smile of relief.

Tomkins adds that the same principle can apply when there is a reduction of pleasure, such as when an enjoyable meal has been completed. This does not mean that smiling is associated in any way with a lack of pleasure, only that a smile is a cardinal sign of reduction of any kind of arousal. Silvan Tomkins writes: 'The theory of any kind of arousal. Silvan Tomkins writes: 'This theory phenomena as disparate as the joy of relieve from pain and the joy of the infant at the sight of its mother.'

BABIES AND SMILING

When babies are newborn they don't smile. But after a very few weeks they start to — and smiling is one of the very first 'human' signs parents look for. Most mothers and fathers want to catch that first smile, and feel rewarded by it for all the hard work they have done, all the sleepless nights and exhaustion.

Though babies do not smile at birth, the muscles that they need for this essential action are already fully formed. Newborns can accurately signal disgust and distress, and can also look startled if appropriate stimuli are applied. But they can't smile.

Occasionally, a newborn baby does form its face into an expression which seems rather like a smile, but, according to paediatricians, these are not real smiles. They are produced by involuntary reactions in the central nervous system. This phenomenon also accounts for the other 'expressions' that sometimes flit across a very young baby's face. These first 'smiles' are not what we would call social smiles, where a baby is showing positive, pleasurable recognition of another human being — the kind of smile this book is concerned with.

Social smiles, according to some authorities, can be noted in certain babies as early as three to four weeks, but not in all infants. A baby will tend to be an early smiler if

he or she is happy, alert, healthy and well looked after. In fact, the more content a baby is, the earlier the first real smiles will be noticed. Most babies produce genuine, reliable, proper smiles by three months, and these smiles — which occur increasingly often — are the first signs of a positive emotion. At this age, a baby will smile not only at its mother, but at any sight resembling its mother's face.

According to Dr Burton L. White, a British paediatrician and author of the book *The First Three Years*, smiles happen mainly because a defenceless baby needs to have some kind of a guarantee that it will gain a positive response from another person. This other person is one who can help to ensure the baby's survival, so it is in the baby's best interests to flash a disarming smile whenever possible. The smile, Dr White continues, is a powerful survival mechanism. There are few adults who are not won over by a baby's brilliant smile.

What is not known for certain is what is going on inside the baby's head to activate the smile in the first place. Is the baby smiling because of happiness, because of a supremely comfortable feeling, or because a familiar face is recognized? Whatever the answer, there seems little doubt that, for infants, smiles are always associated with a positive emotion of some kind. Babies cannot smile and cry at the same time, and the more a baby smiles the less likely it is to cry. The ever-smiling baby, it appears, is far more likely than an infrequent smiler to grow up into a happy child and adult. Babies who smile readily and frequently have more chance of developing stable, friendly and extrovert personalities than those who are constantly grizzling.

Smiling is a powerful way of turning on the body's non-arousal, rest and relaxation system, and this operates in babies just as much as in more mature humans. The earlier and more often a baby's non-arousal systems are activated, the fewer behavioural problems, tantrums and other kinds of negative behaviour are likely to develop.

Babies of three or four months smile only at their mothers or other 'primary carers', as the Americans put it. A baby of this age is unlikely to smile at a complete stranger, though will do so if it thinks the stranger is its mother. Burton White feels that the early smile is an important factor in the mother/baby relationship. 'A smile solidifies the baby's hold on the mother's affection,' he says. Like adults, babies look prettier and more appealing when they smile and this helps us to love them and to be able to put up with the task of bringing them up. The baby's smile is often the adult's sole reward for all the trouble that is being taken — but it is enough.

When a baby first recognizes its mother as a distinct entity, there is a smile. It really does seem as if the emotion the baby most wants to express is happiness, rather than anything else. As babies smile so readily and so quickly, it can be assumed that the natural condition of the human race is happiness. Unhappiness is an unnatural state. That is why it makes us ill, and why happy people rarely suffer from serious illness.

Speaking purely from a physical point of view, smiling is the simplest facial expression we can adopt. Human faces fall readily into smiles, but less readily into expressions of unhappiness or grief. To show negative emotion requires facial contortion which makes people look less attractive than they really are. Happiness is also the only facial expression which has a positive effect on the central nervous system. All others increase arousal, and put a strain of some kind on body systems.

ADULTS AND SMILING

Babies and young children display only one type of smile — the broad, open, friendly smile. As we grow into adults, however, smiling becomes a more complicated activity. Adults smile far less readily than babies, and as we grow up, the ability to smile easily may be lost or perverted.

Adults can display false smiles and natural smiles, happy smiles and miserable smiles, grins, leers, smirks, wry smiles and deceitful smiles. There are open smiles and guarded smiles, smiles that reveal the teeth, and others where the mouth is kept closed. There are 'professional' cheesecake smiles, and those shared with loved ones. There are also the private smiles triggered by something which we — but not necessarily anybody else — find funny. There is the smile that explodes into laughter, and the helpless giggle. We can also, if necessary, put forced smiles on our faces.

Although the smile is the easiest and most natural facial expression, it can convey a multitude of different meanings. In this, it is different again from all other human facial expressions. There is only one look of surprise, one look of fear, one of sadness. But there are very many different types of smile, each activated by its own stimulus.

Complex smiles have been minutely analysed, notably by Professor Ekman, who has pioneered world research into smiling and laughter. He has described three main types of smile: the *felt* smile, the *false* smile and the *miserable* smile. Once you know what to look for, he says, it is quite easy to distinguish between these different types of smile. They are all occasioned by quite separate emotions, and will, therefore, call particular muscles and groups of muscles into play. Few people would mistake a genuinely happy smile for a miserable smile, but it is not

always easy to distinguish between a felt smile and a false smile. There are, however, some giveaway signs which even the most practised actor and facial deceiver cannot hide, because the muscles which activate these smiles are not capable of complete control.

It appears that different neural pathways are involved in involuntary and voluntary smiles, even though they may not necessarily differ in outward appearance. Paul Ekman and two co-workers have compared the expressions of those who smile on request with those of people who are smiling naturally in response to a joke or funny event. The most striking difference seems to be in the amount of symmetry in the face. Deliberate smiles are far more asymmetrical or 'sideways' than genuine smiles, and also last for longer on the face. If somebody holds a smile for just that second or two longer than the occasion seems to justify, then you can be sure they are flashing a false smile at you. A false smile is, by definition, one put on the face deliberately in order to mislead other people, and make them believe an emotion is being felt when it is not. A false smile also, according to researchers, takes far longer than a real one to spread across the face.

Paul Ekman has defined the three main types of smiles thus: a *felt* smile, he says, is one where there is 'spontaneous overflow of positive emotion', whereas a *false* smile is a 'deliberate attempt to simulate positive emotion'. A *miserable* smile is 'an acknowledgement of a miserable state which is perceived as such by others'. The felt smile, he says, is a genuine expression of some kind of positive emotion and therefore occurs after the emotional state has been experienced. These emotions include pleasure from stimulation of any kind, whether this is visual, auditory, or a taste sensation. Affectionate touching can also bring forth the felt smile. Real smiles can spread across the face as relief from pain or uncomfortable pressure of some kind.

In order to measure certain types of smile, and distinguish them from each other, Professor Ekman developed what he has called the Facial Action Coding

System (FACS). This is a complicated form of measuring chart which allows for measurement of all the minutiae of facial behaviour. Armed with this system, Ekman has been able to discover that the muscles involved in felt smiles are somewhat different from those used when a false smile is called for.

THE FELT SMILE

Felt smiles bring forth the spontaneous action of two main muscles. One is the zygomatic major, already mentioned, which pulls up the corners of the lip towards the cheekbone. The other muscle usually involved in genuine smiles is the *orbicularis oculi* which raises the cheek and gathers the skin inwards from the eye socket. After studying many thousands of genuine smiles, and subjecting them to his measuring chart, Ekman was able to come to the conclusion that the level of positive emotion felt is always reflected in the action of these two muscles. The more intense the emotion, the more pleasurable the experience, the greater the action of these muscles. The felt smile can of course vary greatly, from a small, shy smile to a huge grin and helpless laughter. But the muscles involved will be the same.

It was Darwin who first discovered that the action of the zygomatic major muscle was central to the expression of positive emotional experience, and most subsequent scientific research has been built on the foundations he established.

The felt smile has a very fixed duration, of between two-thirds of a second and four seconds in length. When the positive feelings are fairly weak, there are only slight contractions of the muscles, but when the emotions are strong, the muscles respond accordingly. However strong the feelings, though, genuine smiles are seldom held for more than four seconds.

FALSE SMILES

When we come to analyse false smiles, we find they are
phony through and through. No positive emotion
accompanies the grin, however broad the smile might be.
And however much the smilers may want you to believe
their smile is genuine, they will never be able to fool the
experts. Though the false smile closely mimics the real
one, it is usually employed in order to cover up negative
emotions. False smiles are seen on the faces of politicians
when they learn they have not won the election, on the
faces of athletes who come second or third rather than
first, and on the faces of failed Miss World contestants.

People also flash false smiles when they only pretend to
be pleased to see you. Door-to-door salesmen (the good
ones) have perfected false smiles. What will be absent
from all these smiles is warmth or genuine happiness, and
it will show on the face. Actors, and those whose job
requires them to cover up negative emotions, often
become very practised at putting on a smile they do not
feel. Nevertheless, it is not the same thing, and as such
will not convey the same meaning to an onlooker.

It is noticeable that, when a smile is false, the
orbicularis oculi muscles round the eyes do not come into
play. Nobody can disguise this, however much they
practise smiling. It seems that the *orbicularis oculi* muscles
are simply not under control of the brain, and can only
be activated when there is genuine emotion. If you want to
ascertain whether somebody is smiling genuinely, don't
look so much at the mouth as round the eyes. If they are
not creased up and the expression in them is dead and
lifeless, you can be certain you are witnessing a false
smile.

MISERABLE SMILES

The miserable smile does not indicate a false emotion, but
spreads across the face to indicate to observers that the
subject is not happy. The miserable smile is intended to

convey a feeling of unhappiness or distress and is
characterized, according to Ekman, by considerable
asymmetry. In other words, the miserable smile will be
very lopsided.

EYE CONTACT

In his book *Body Language*, Australian management
consultant Allan Pease explains the importance of eye
contact, and how it is related to the warmth or otherwise
of a smile. When people are feeling angry and negative —
even when they try to disguise it — the pupils contract.
Even the biggest false smile in the world cannot
counteract the size of the pupils. But when a person is
happy or excited, the pupils may dilate by up to four
times their natural size. Pease uses the example of being
in love. If a woman truly loves a man, he says, she will
unconsciously dilate her pupils at him and he will, also
unconsciously, accurately decode this signal.

We have largely lost, or forgotten, the ancient art of
pupil-watching, but it remains one of the most accurate
indicators of a state of mind. When a person is being
dishonest but is trying to hide this with a large broad grin,

such as exemplified by the evil J.R. in the TV soap *Dallas*, the eyes will meet those of the interlocutor less than two-thirds of the time and the pupils will stay tiny. The more genuine an expression is, the more truly felt a positive emotion, the more eye contact there will be. Warmth is underlined by pupil size but this, like the muscles round the eyes, cannot be controlled by the brain. Pupils expand and contract in size involuntarily. Eyes are total giveaways, far more than mouths.

The ancient Chinese, according to Pease, made a big thing of pupil-watching when trading. Gem traders used to look into the eyes of people to whom they were trying to sell their wares. If the pupils became big, then the potential buyer was interested, and the price could be increased with impunity. Pease speculates that one reason why the late shipping magnate Aristotle Onassis always wore dark glasses was so that his eyes would never give him away during delicate business transactions.

There are other observable differences between the felt and the false smile. These happen even when the deceitful smiler tries to make the smile genuine by consciously recalling a positive emotion. This is a favourite trick used by actors to give credibility to their performances on stage or screen. The false smile, however, always, always, comes just that bit too early or too late. You can tell when somebody does not get a joke, or does not find it funny, by the length of time that the smile takes to appear. When a smile is genuine, it appears at exactly the right moment — because, again, it cannot be controlled by the brain or mind. Whenever a joke is found to be funny, there is always a precise and exact moment when laughter is indicated.

LEARNING FROM PEOPLE'S EXPRESSIONS

Once you know how to read it, the face can become an accurate conveyer of information. Even in repose the face is informative, and few people can hide what they really feel. Though Shakespeare's Duncan, in *Macbeth*, may have felt there was no art to find the mind's construction in the face, modern scientific discoveries and instruments have now proved him wrong. Every single nuance, every tiny shade of expression that spreads across a human face has a distinct and special meaning. Researchers have now discovered that more than a thousand different facial expressions are possible.

But there is still much that we don't know. There is much to learn, for example, about how the different facial expressions are related to emotion. Does the emotion come first, or the expression? Can certain expressions alter emotions for better or for worse? If you put on a smile, and decide to look on the bright side, even though you are feeling miserable, can this affect the way you feel? It should be said here that putting on a smile when you feel sad inside is not the same as a false smile — it is not intended to mislead, but is a way of trying to help you feel better about things.

The message of this book is that facial expressions actually do alter emotions, and that in time, like Beerbohm's Happy Hypocrite, you feel in tune with your predominant expression. Somebody who goes around with a perpetual poker face or a miserable expression will probably — in time at least — come to feel quite different emotions from people who are jolly and cheerful, or who try to look so. In order to *be* happy you first have to try and *look* happy.

Smiling is, as all beauticians know, a potent beauty treatment. There is a very logical reason why people who smile a lot seem to have the secret of eternal youth. It's not anything magic, but simply to do with the muscles involved in pulling different facial expressions. In smiling, as we have seen, only one major muscle is used, whereas in the expression of all the negative emotions such as anxiety, fear, disgust and sadness, very many more muscles are involved. For every facial expression except smiling, the face has to be contorted. The more the face is twisted up into unhappy expression, the sooner these wrinkles will turn into permanent lines, which are ageing as well as offputting and unattractive.

Our facial muscles were designed by nature to smile, rather than to express discontented or unhappy emotions. A major experiment carried out as long ago as 1964 demonstrated this conclusively. A researcher in the USA asked a number of actors to simulate three 'pure' emotions — happiness, surprise and anger. Photos were taken of each expression, and then shown to people who were asked to guess which emotion was being conveyed by the expression. There was high agreement — over 70 per cent — on the expressions that were meant to convey happiness, but not with either of the other emotions. The actors were then asked to contort their faces into various blends of all three emotions. Again, there was no particular agreement on which emotion was intended by the expression.

People can instantly recognize a smile, and know that it conveys, or is meant to convey, an emotion of happiness. But interpreting other emotions is far more difficult. An identical facial expression was read by some people as disgust, by others as anger. We can, of course, see clearly when people are displeased, or not happy, but it is not always clear whether they are nervous, afraid, startled or angry. This, together with other experiments which will be described in subsequent chapters, seems to indicate that happiness is the purest, most unalloyed expression, the one we can most readily recognize. There is only one facial expression which conveys happiness, and that is smiling. What's more, it is universal. In his travels, Darwin discovered that smiling was the only expression which was recognized instantly all over the world.

In some studies, people of different races and from quite different cultures have been asked to look at sets of photographs showing a range of expressions, and decide which emotion was being conveyed. All over the world, there was by far the highest agreement for happiness. It is the most accurately judged of all facial expressions, and all races smile to show they are happy or pleased. Happiness always comes top of any scale of this type, and has done so ever since this kind of study was first mounted about a century ago.

Whether rightly or wrongly, those who smile a lot are perceived as having different kinds of personalities from people who habitually frown or look sad. Constant smilers are seen as friendly and outgoing, easy to get along with, extrovert, loving, warm and giving. Conversely, people who find it difficult to smile tend to be viewed as withdrawn, introvert, reserved, shy, withholding and cold. We are instinctively drawn to people who smile a lot. They seem 'nicer' than those who never, or rarely smile.

Advertisers know this, of course, and sell their products by associating them in the minds of the consumer with smiling faces. The impression conveyed is that using the particular product either makes people happy, or that only happy, likeable people use it. Smiling is particularly noticeable in alcohol advertisments. Martini drinkers are always smiling and laughing and having a good time. Smiles are also potent sellers of very many soft drinks, too.

TO SUM UP

Smiling is, by one definition, simply baring the teeth. But that's not the whole story. Try baring your teeth in a fierce expression, and then try baring them in a smile. You will soon discover that you actually feel different when putting on the two expressions. The fierce teeth-baring face makes you feel instantly aggressive and hostile, even though you may not have felt this before assuming the expression. The smile, by contrast, makes you feel immediately happier, more gentle and at peace.

The ability to smile is a gift given to all humans, but to no other creature on earth. It is intended to enable humans to reach out to each other, to establish friendly contact, to come closer and to get on with each other. Smiling is understood everywhere: it is the most universal human language. If you were to meet a strange race of people, you would soon know whether they were hostile or friendly by the readiness or otherwise of their smiles. People who are hostile to each other do not smile. Smiles can break down international and language barriers, and establish close contacts even when it is not possible to communicate in words. This is because smiles say so much.

Smiling is the most *human* of all activities; it is the most natural facial expression there is. Smiling costs nothing and has no adverse side effects. It's something anybody can do. The trouble is, most adults don't smile nearly enough.

2.
WHAT IS LAUGHTER?

Humans are the only creatures who can smile, and the only animals who can laugh. But why are we blessed with this peculiar ability? It is a question that has occupied scientists and philosophers for many hundreds of years. Since we are able to laugh, they have argued, it must stand to reason that laughter serves an important purpose. But just what is that purpose?

On the face of it, it would seem as though we are able to manage perfectly well without laughter in our lives. We do not need to be able to laugh in order to survive in any physical sense and we could, conceivably, live without laughing at all. But the fact is, we do laugh. Even the saddest people will laugh on occasion, and there probably has not been a human born who has not laughed at some time.

As humans, we are all born with an innate ability to laugh, and this ability manifests itself long before speech and language have been acquired. We do not have to learn how to laugh, and we don't do it just to imitate other people. Babies start to chuckle long before their brains are able to find anything to laugh about, so laughter is not always connected with cerebral amusement.

Some authorities have suggested that laughter is strongly developed in humans because of the long dependency we have as children. This dependency requires powerful signs to release, control and reward the adults who are taking care of the infant — to encourage them to continue with their task, presumably. So, according to one definition, laughter has developed in humans as a survival mechanism.

Laughter, as we know, relieves tension and makes people feel happier than before. Laughter is associated with feeling good, rather than feeling bad. So it seems as though laughter must serve some deep therapeutic purpose which is beneficial to humans. Since animals cannot laugh, it may be argued, they simply don't need to laugh. Perhaps they do not build up the kind of tension that can be released and removed by laughter.

From earliest times, laughter has been held in high esteem. People who can make others laugh have been among the most highly paid and highly prized members of society. In medieval and Tudor times the court jester enjoyed a highly privileged position and, as long as he kept people laughing, could get away with a great deal — as indeed can our present-day comedians, So much do we want to be made to laugh that we feel bitterly disappointed when a comedy show turns out not to be funny after all. A witty person is always welcome in any gathering (provided the wit does not turn into biting sarcasm aimed at others present).

We all know, instinctively, that laughter is more than just a noise we make on certain occasions. It is actually physically enjoyable to laugh, and most of us will feel better inside after a good bout of laughter. As we also know, the act of laughter is infectious. If we see somebody laughing helplessly, it is difficult not to join in, even though we may have no idea what they are laughing about. We always look forward to meeting people who can make us laugh, who always have a cheery word, who can see the funny side of things and don't take every aspect of life too seriously. We enjoy being with these people so long as the laughter is genuine.

WHEN LAUGHTER ISN'T FUNNY

Nervous giggles, laughing at, rather than with, people, false laughter which is not engendered by an amusing

He always gets them rolling in the aisles

situation, laughing at things which are not funny, such as mental and physical handicap, hysterical laughter — all these produce an uneasy, stressful feeling in those who are forced to listen. Our laughter antennae are so accurate that we can instantly tell the difference between genuine and forced laughter, between laughter that arises out of humour and happiness, and that which indicates tension and fear.

There are many different types of laughter, and each of these is likely to produce different feelings in both those who laugh and those who are listening. There is the loud bellow — often perpetrated by men — which does not make us feel amused at all. In fact, it can have the opposite effect and be quite frightening. People who laugh loudly at their own jokes and quips are not usually amusing company, nor are those who laugh at the misfortunes of others. Habitual gigglers are not amusing either, and a gaggle or children shrieking on a bus or other confined public place provokes only annoyance and irritation in those within earshot.

There is also the type of laughter — again not funny — which arises out of particularly tense situations such as a funeral. You may feel like laughing at a funeral, not because the occasion is in any way amusing, but because it is highly awkward and uncomfortable. One potent property of laughter is that it enables us to shed some of the tensions which may have built up during a difficult situation.

Several philosophers and psychiatrists, among them Freud, Kant and Herbert Spencer, see laughter essentially as a means of discharging surplus tension or mental excitation. Laughter, they say, restores normal equilibrium. We laugh at the incongruous, at things which don't seem quite to fit and which, although they may not be actually funny, are nevertheless peculiar. Funerals would fit into this category.

The bellower in the pub, the giggling teenager, the chap who guffaws nervously and continuously at his own jokes are all people who are releasing some kind of long-held tension in themselves. When they laugh like this, they are not intending to convey amusement, and others around them do not laugh. But the laughter nevertheless serves a purpose in dissipating anxiety and tension.

One reason we like people who laugh a lot is because in order to laugh you have to smile, and smiling faces are always far more attractive than grim, fierce ones. Some scientists have defined smiling as a 'low-intensity laugh', and it could be argued that laughter is just one stage on from smiling. For though you can smile without laughing, it is impossible to laugh without smiling. In order to discharge itself, laughter must have a smiling face. People who do try to laugh without smiling — such as on finding themselves in a situation where laughter is inapproriate — often become acutely uncomfortable, and eventually feel as though they will burst. It is very difficult to stop yourself from laughing when you have a great desire to do so.

We like people who laugh easily because we are not afraid of them. If people want to appear stern, serious and authoritative, they do not usually laugh. When as a schoolchild, you were summoned to see the head teacher,

it was not an occasion for laughter. Managers do not normally laugh when they are giving a worker the sack, or announcing the closure of a company. Prime Ministers do not laugh when they announce a war, judges do not laugh when they are pronouncing a life sentence. Former lovers do not laugh when they are about to part for ever. If these people did laugh on such occasions, we would tend not to believe what they were saying, and we might take no notice of them.

There are some situations in life which nobody is meant to find funny, and where anybody laughing would be regarded with the utmost suspicion, if not as an outright lunatic. When people laugh in unsuitable situations, it is often assumed they are mentally unbalanced, and that their laughter comes from a disordered sense of propriety.

LAUGHTER AND INTELLIGENCE

Though those who laugh readily are usually popular in company, they may also run the danger of being regarded as frivolous or empty-headed. For, unfortunately, easy laughter is associated with a certain lack of intelligence. Though we enjoy the company of comedians, and find their humour irresistible, most of us would feel we wouldn't want them running the country. It might be that they couldn't take anything seriously.

We also feel that those who laugh a lot are somehow less intelligent than the ever-serious person. We choose as politicians and world leaders, on the whole, people who are not noted for their easy laughter and ability to crack a joke in all situations. The comedians, whether professional or not, are seen as the lightweights in our society, the comic relief, rather than the real stuff of life. They are the ones who leaven the seriousness, who provide the seasoning in our diet.

Light relief in the form of cartoons is provided in most newspapers, but it is the serious commentators who are the most heeded. We like to be made to laugh, but we don't usually take much notice of what comedians say. Intelligence levels have come to be equated with seriousness, which is one reason why the more seriously and weightily you say something, the more brainpower you are assumed to have.

In fact, as I shall hope to show in this book, it is the people who can smile and laugh a lot who are actually the most intelligent, as they are the ones who best understand how essential laughter is to health, happiness and keeping things in proportion. There is now evidence to show that, if you can laugh at troubles, whether financial, medical or emotional, the laughter can actually help to send them away.

We all know, theoretically at least, that worrying about a problem does nothing to solve it or make it go away but that the more we worry, the worse it gets. We are soon carrying a double burden, consisting of the problem and the worry on top of it. By laughing at troubles, we are saying that we will not allow that big dark cloud of worry to descend and ruin everything. This does not mean we are unwilling to face problems, or to seek a solution, but that we are able to be philosophical and detached about them.

The poet Longfellow wrote: 'Life is real, life is earnest,' by which he probably meant that life is serious. In fact, life should be fun. The more happiness we can create in ourselves and others, the better our world will be. It is no use always expecting that others will be there to make us laugh; we must learn to laugh ourselves, and most of all, at ourselves.

There is absolutely no doubt about this. If politicians at summit meetings could laugh more, instead of being permanently grim-faced and pessimistic about 'finding a solution', if they could smile at each other instead of being severe, they would find that solutions presented themselves. If unions and management could laugh more round the negotiating table, settlements that pleased all could be arrived at more quickly and more pleasantly.

Laughter, which is essentially a shared activity, as in the old proverb, 'Laugh and the world laughs with you, weep and you weep alone,' brings people together, even when they may have little else in common. Serious, set faces by contrast keep people apart and hostile to each other. A grim face says that you are keeping your distance and do not want to come closer. It is impossible to hate somebody and laugh with them at the same time.

Laughter implies friendliness, a willingness to reach out to the other person. It is essentially a giving activity, whereas to be serious means you are giving nothing away. There is a place for the inscrutable expression, of course, but when you are not giving much away, there is always the danger that others will misinterpret your intentions.

Those who can genuinely smile and laugh are handing out an invisible olive branch. They are saying, in effect: I mean you no hearm. They are saying: I'm friendly with you, I'm on your side. Those who can smile and laugh in potentially fraught situations are the real geniuses, the truly creative people in our society, since they are saying: I am not afraid. It often takes a great deal of courage to laugh at a situation, to smile when others appear hostile and unfriendly, and to refuse to be devastated when things go wrong.

Shakespeare knew that people who can smile and laugh are superior beings. He often put the wisest and wittiest

sayings into the mouths of the fools in his plays. The
jesters might be called fools and clowns, but they are
usually the ones who see through to the reality of the
situation. One reason they are able to do this is because
they remain detached and objective, and do not get
caught up in fraught emotions and turbulent goings-on.
Shakespeare's fools are clever, amusing, attractive, warm
and loyal people.

LAUGHING IS GOOD FOR YOU

As one might imagine, any activity that helps to make the
world a more pleasant place to live actually does people
good as well. Laughter is not just a meaningless noise that
emanates from the mouth to indicate amusement or as the
Oxford English Dictionary has it, 'A spasmodic utterance
associated with mirth, holding the sides, etc.'. Laughter as
a physiological activity actually has far-reaching effects on
body systems.

The act of laughing serves to get more oxygen into the
lungs, deepening breathing, which in turn makes the
circulation more effective and less sluggish. One French
doctor, Pierre Vachet, who has studied the physiology of
laughing for many years, came to the conclusion that
laughter expands the blood vessels, and sends more blood
racing to the extremities. So those who suffer from cold
hands and feet should perhaps try laughing instead of
piling on the socks and gloves. Laughing creates internal
warmth. As it sends more oxygen racing to every cell in
the body, laughter can also serve to speed tissue healing
and, according to Vachet, stabilize many body functions,
helping to strengthen them against infection and
abnormal growths. Laughter can also reduce heart rate
and stimulate the appetite, says another expert, French
neurologist Henri Rubinstein.

It also seems that laughter can improve the body's
delicate hormonal balance. It appears to stimulate the
production of beta-endorphins, natural painkillers
produced in the brain. Some French researchers who

believe in the power of laughter as a medicine have even hypothesized that those who laugh a lot are far less prone to digestive disorders and stomach ulcers than people who find it hard to laugh. The point about laughter, which has been called 'stationary jogging', is that it provides good exercise for all the internal systems, and gets everything on the move again. Fear, tension and anxiety tend to make the body's systems seize up and work less effectively than they should.

Laughter helps our system to purge itself of rubbish such as excess cholesterol and other unwanted fats. It also helps to clear rubbish from the mind by stimulating production of the natural painkillers. Whenever we can laugh at a problem we are actually purging ourselves of the worry it causes, and in the resulting clarity we will be able to find the right solution.

MIND AND MATTER

We cannot know exactly, how far our thoughts affect our bodies and influence physical health, but all the research

He's taken up stationary jogging

into stress, depression and other negative mental states points to the fact that whatever affects the mind will also eventually affect the body.

We do know that thoughts can trigger the production of hormones, which are then sent coursing round the body. Long-held mental tensions, as we now understand, can eventually manifest themselves as some physical complaint. We know that such conditions as chronic backache, migraine, ulcers and digestive problems are all closely linked with states of mind. A growing number of authorities now also believe that serious, life-threatening diseases such as cancer and heart disease are intimately affected by a person's state of mind, outlook and attitude. With cancer victims, doctors have discovered that a change of attitude from negative to positive is often the very first step in the healing process.

One London doctor, Steven Greer, realized several years ago that cancer patients who were determined to fight their disease had far better results than those who passively accepted it or succumbed to fear. When we are anxious and afraid, or in physical pain, we tense up and become rigid.

Laughter, of course, promotes relaxation. It is actually impossible to be rigid when you laugh, as laughter is a sensation that runs through the whole body, making you shake and move about. This jolting-up is good for people. When we laugh, all our body systems are shaken up and tension is released. Laughter is a relaxing activity in itself, and could do more good than all the exercises, aerobics and mental tricks people are currently using to try and help them to relax.

Sometimes, of course, it can be acutely uncomfortable to laugh. I can remember, just after having had a baby, listening to an unintentionally very funny conversation taking place by the next bed. I very much wanted to laugh, and could hardly stop myself, but was nervous of laughing in case I broke my stitches. Some people, particularly young women, have experienced the rather embarrassing and not at all uncommon problem of 'giggle incontinence', where helpless laughter makes them wet themselves. That is what happens with genuine laughter — sometimes the mind cannot control the body systems, and the results may be embarrassing or uncomfortable. Even so, that doesn't mean laughter is a bad activity.

When overcome with laughter, we often have no choice but to let ourselves go. We lose our dignity, we flail around, we forget momentarily how we are sitting or standing, and give in completely to the fit of laughter while it lasts. Sometimes we simply don't have the choice. Something strikes us as so funny on that particular occasion that all we can do is to continue laughing until it has subsided. Henri Rubinstein states in his research papers that laughter is the best relaxant there is — as even one minute of laughter can give the body up to 45 minutes of therapeutic relaxation. Laughter, it appears, has much the same effect on the body as regular physical exercise, in that the 'high' produced goes on working long after the exercise is over. Laughter is, after all, another form of bodily exercise. For people who are ill, or confined to bed or a wheelchair, laughter may be the only exercise they are able to take.

We have been very slow to acknowledge the therapeutic benefits of laughter. It is something we can all do, and it is absolutely free and highly effective. Yet despite — perhaps because of — its openness to all, laughter has not been prized as it should be. The latest edition of the *Encyclopedia Britannica* defines laughter as a simple reflex action:

> Spontaneous laughter is a motor reflex produced by the co-ordinated contraction of 15 facial muscles in a stereotyped pattern, and accompanied by altered breathing. Electrical stimulation of the main lifting muscle of the upper lip, the zygomatic major, with currents of varying intensity, produces facial expressions ranging from the faint smile ... to contortions typical of explosive laughter ... Laughter is a reflex, but unique in that it has no apparent biological function. One might call it a luxury reflex. Its only function seems to be a relief from tension.

The giveaway, of course, is contained in the last sentence. After saying that it has no biological function,

the encyclopedia goes on to state that it gives relief from tension. And there we have it. The writer of this entry obviously thinks that relief from tension is not a very important matter. My own belief — and that of a growing number of researchers, doctors and scientists the world over — is that tension is our greatest threat to health, both mental and physical. It therefore stands to reason that anything that helps to relieve tension must be of potent therapeutic value.

THE RELIEF OF TENSION

We need laughter as a safety valve. Animals have no need of the function because, on the whole, they experience less mental stress than we do. Their minds do not cause them to worry and fret over a situation. They experience neither guilt nor worry, and carry no mental burdens around with them. They live for the moment. One can, of course, point to instances where animals do suffer fear and tension, such as when being captured, or when about to be slaughtered or otherwise ill-treated. But these situations are not of the animals' making. They are imposed on them by humans.

We humans suffer because we make ourselves suffer, and we also cause other people to suffer. That is why we need laughter so much, and why laughter has such an important biological significance. There exists no scientific evidence to confirm that those who laugh most live longest, but there is certainly plenty of evidence to suggest that happy people — those who are in harmony with themselves and their environment — live longer than those who hate and are miserable.

You can't laugh much if you hate. And hatred, as Iris Murdoch observes in her novel *The Good Apprentice*, harms only the hater, not the object of the hatred. Negative emotions cause increased production of stress hormones, which in turn can attack the body's defence system and reduce resistance to all illnesses.

Stress expert Dr Malcolm Carruthers has stated on

many occasions that the important factor in heart disease is not so much what you are eating as what is eating you. The story below is a dramatic example of how hatred and jealousy can kill. A woman who was once my boss was consumed with hatred and hostility. She was never known to laugh or smile, but went around bent-shouldered and with a permanent scowl on her face. She appeared to hate everybody, and certainly she was the least popular person in the company. Few people were surprised when, at the early age of 50, she died riddled with cancer. Her hatred had consumed her. Other people get ill and die because they allow exhaustion, stress at work, family problems or their own fears to take a hold on them until they feel they cannot cope with life any more.

Those who are able to retain their ability to laugh are, I suggest, people who are allowing positive rather than negative emotions to surface and show themselves. They have learned that happiness and laughter make it possible to stay free from illness, and to be outgoing and giving. Those who are able to give, and who can enjoy sharing the good things of life, usually remain free from illness.

LAUGHTER IS POSITIVE

In order to remain healthy, it is essential to be able to share, and those who can laugh are sharers. A few examples here will show what I mean by sharing and giving.

Barbara Cartland, the romantic novelist who is as old as the century, is still writing 20 or more novels a year. She is also very forthcoming with quotes and interviews, and is always game to try something new. All her life she has consciously tried to be positive, and we always see pictures of her looking happy and contented. Instead of moaning about how things aren't what they used to be, as so many old people do, Barbara Cartland is still promoting her message, that love conquers all. Her daughter Raine, the Countess of Spencer, has a similarly positive attitude to life, and, it is said, actually willed her husband, Lord

Spencer, to recover from a heart attack. Her positive attitude gave him the strength and courage to pull through. The novelist Jilly Cooper is also always pictured smiling and laughing, and looking as though she is having a good time.

We may choose to see such people as 'lightweight', but we do not always remember that those who add joy and happiness, rather than misery and despair, are actually life's healers. As long ago as the 18th century the writer Jonathan Swift, not himself the merriest of men it must be admitted, prescribed the best healers in the world to be 'Dr Diet, Dr Quiet and Dr Merriman'. In other words, healing comes from within, it is within our powers to heal ourselves.

Amusement and laughter are not just involuntary reflexes, on a level with twitching or blinking, activities that mean nothing and serve no useful purpose. They are, as scientists are now discovering, the happy end result of a harmonious balance between the sympathetic and the parasympathetic nervous systems, between the voluntary and the involuntary actions of the body.

It is not always realized just how much we are able to influence the workings of our own bodies. We can create harmony by laughing and smiling — in other words, by engaging in activities the body likes and welcomes. Or we can set body systems against each other by wallowing in negative emotions that put the body in a perpetual state of war and conflict against itself. Just as nations cannot long survive when there is civil war, nor can the body — and illness must eventually result when we are no longer able to laugh and smile, when our minds are so burdened that we do not feel like laughing.

Laughing enables us to see the world around us more realistically. It enables us to see through pretensions and egotism, through ruthless greed and ambition, all things that are destructive rather than constructive. Laughter is always accompanied by beneficial physiological changes that anybody can observe, such as sparkling eyes and the brightening of the whole personality. Negative emotions and states of mind can lead to chronic high blood pressure. If those who suffered from high blood pressure could learn to laugh more, they would probably find their blood pressure normalized without having to resort to pills with unwelcome side effects. Increased blood pressure, except perhaps in pregnant women, is almost always the result of excess mental tension and anxiety. This boosts the heart rate, making the sufferer permanently keyed up for a crisis that may never happen.

TICKLISHNESS AND TEARFULNESS

There are, of course, various kinds of laughter that are not associated with any kind of amusement. One of these is laughter that results from being tickled. Another is the kind of laughter that comes when we are basically unhappy and burst into tears. How are these types of laughter distinguished from happy laughter? After all, the physiological mechanisms must be the same.

The laughter that results from being tickled is a phenomenon that has been studied by many scientists. In his book *The Diseases of Civilization*, Dr Brian Inglis

No, no, anything but the feather!

quotes Arthur Koestler as observing that tickling is a form of mock attack, and that people only laugh when they are being tickled as they perceive it as a 'caress in mildly aggressive disguise'.

Other researchers have noted that tickling only provokes laughter in certain distinct body areas, such as the soles of the feet, underneath the arms, and around the ribs. These are the areas which are abundantly supplied with lots of protective nerve endings and are, therefore, especially sensitive to attack. We laugh when we are being tickled because the body's defence systems are being alerted, but the mind perceives that no harm is being done. If the tickling starts to hurt, the laughter does not continue.

Even though we may not be consciously happy when being tickled, it seems as though the act of laughter serves to jolt us out of negative emotion and turn tears to happiness. If children can be made to laugh through being tickled, they will often forget the cause of their distress, and become happy. The laughter that results from tickling can provide a breathing space, which enables a negative mood to be turned into a cheerful mood.

Children are, of course, far more ticklish than adults. There has been no satisfactory explanation as to why ticklishness is lost with advancing years. It could be that, as we grow into adulthood, we find increasingly less to laugh about, and tend to take everything more seriously, so that the ability to laugh when being tickled is lost.

Laughter that is mixed with crying and hysterical laughter are two kinds of laughter that are not generally associated with being happy. Even so, both seem to serve the same purpose of relieving stress and tension. Crying, particularly, can be very therapeutic. We know instinctively that crying can help to get grief and worries out of the system, and now science can tell us why. Apparently, it has much to do with the tears themselves. In 1986 the world's first Congress on Tears was held in Dallas, Texas. At the conference, scientists presented papers on the different kinds of tears. It seems that tears that result from misery or from 'crying with laughter' have a quite different chemical composition from those which are produced as a result of peeling onions or walking out on a windy day.

Tears which are produced as the result of emotion contain an enkaphalin, a naturally produced painkiller. This substance is one of the body's own defences against pain and uncomfortable emotions. Crying enables extra quantities of enkaphalin to be produced, and thus helps us to overcome pain and sorrow.

The function of hysterical or demented laughter is also the release of tension, though the sound of hysterical laughter may be uncomfortable for those who have to listen to it. When we find something hysterically funny, or fall about laughing and end up crying, this whole sequence can be a form of catharsis, a method of enabling pent-up emotions to surface and then disappear. This kind of laughter, often associated with mental illness, may have little to do with being happy, but there seems no doubt that people feel better afterwards.

FITS OF LAUGHTER

Psychiatrists have often noted the similarity between fits, as in epileptic fits, and ecstasy, which may include laughter. The idea that a kind of 'brainstorm' produces therapeutic release led to the development of ECT — electro-convulsive therapy — as a treatment for certain forms of mental illness and depression. ECT induces artificially something resembling an epileptic fit, but it has now been largely discredited, and is gradually being phased out of psychiatric hospitals.

Experts today believe that there is a great difference between ecstatic and epileptic fits which occur naturally, and those which are artificially induced by means of electrical currents. The natural fit may be entirely necessary in order to discharge mental waste matter which has somehow been allowed to build up in the system. The induced fit is an attempt by outsiders to cure a condition seen as anti-social, and it is unlikely that it causes the same internal changes.

It is becoming clear that therapeutic laughter — or the kind of noise and facial expression we associate with release of some kind — has to come from within and be produced naturally. Artificially induced replicas of the real thing do not work, and can be positively dangerous. When we speak of smiling and laughter as therapy, we do not therefore include artificially induced fits where the patient is unconscious and knows nothing of the proceedings until they are over. In order to be genuinely therapeutic, laughter — whatever its cause — has to be produced by the patient.

LAUGHTER ADDICTION

It is said that anything that may lead to addictive behaviour is bad. Examples include smoking, drinking and eating to excess, and taking psychoactive drugs. Addictive substances are bad because they eventually take over the person, gaining control of the personality, until everything in life becomes reduced to feeding the addiction.

But, just as we can develop bad habits, it is possible to cultivate good ones, and allow them to become ingrained. There is no better habit to get into than that of smiling and laughter — not inappropriately or nervously of course — but when conditions are suitable. There is also evidence to suggest that people who consciously try to make themselves smile and laugh, even when they feel miserable inside, can bring about powerful positive mood changes. If people try to show positive reactions instead of negative ones, this will eventually become part of their personality. Start to laugh and in time you will actually become happier. The mind and intellect will clear, and things won't seem so bad. Anybody who doubts the truth of this should try it and see.

3.
HAVING A SENSE OF HUMOUR

When asked which quality they prize most in a man, women will invariably reply: a sense of humour. Everything else — looks, money, status — is considered less important. Men also value a sense of humour in a woman, though not to the same extent.

Why should humour be seen as so important, even vital, particularly in a man? And how does having a sense of humour relate to staying healthy and happy? Basically, people with a sense of humour have retained the ability to laugh at themselves, and have learnt not to take themselves too seriously. When somebody has a sense of humour, it means they do not have an inflated and unrealistic sense of their own importance. For some reason, men have a greater tendency to take themselves too seriously, and to imagine they are more important than they really are. This is why women like humour: a pompous, deadly serious man is not much fun to live with.

From the point of view of health, an over-inflated ego and sense of self can lead to a physical rigidity which may cause bad backs, headaches, ulcers, even cancer and heart disease. Why? Simply because when people become over-serious and unable to discharge tension with humour, the tension remains contained within them. In time, this can cause severe health problems.

The traditional, militaristic public school stiff-upper-lip idea is not conducive to good health since it requires the pretence that problems do not exist or that, unacknowledged, they will fade away. People who have a sense of humour acknowledge the existence of difficult situations, but refuse to be made nervous or ill by them.

Most illness springs initially from fear, and humour dispels fear. Those who go around being fearful do not, on the whole, have a well-developed sense of humour. The ability to laugh, both at oneself and at the ridiculousness of the world, serves to cast out fear. To make a joke about something means you have faced up to the fear of it, and defused it before it can build into a huge dark cloud over your head. A well-timed joke provides a safety valve, an outlet whereby our minds and bodies can return to normality.

THE SAD JOKERS

Having a sense of humour is not always the same thing as being able to make jokes. American humorist Dorothy Parker was one of the wittiest women of the century, yet she was never happy. At the end of her life, poor, ill and alone, she was asked the source of her humour, and replied: 'I was just a little Jewish girl trying to be smart.'

Many of Dorothy Parker's witticisms have passed into common parlance, so neat and apt are they. Her most famous quip is: 'Men never make passes at girls wearing glasses,' but her many other renowned lines (such as: 'One more drink and I'll be under the host;' 'If all those girls were laid end to end I shouldn't be a bit surprised') were just tossed off more or less spontaneously.

Yet for all her wit and sparkle, by the time she died Dorothy Parker was almost forgotten and friendless. Along with her biting wit, she possessed a great ability to alienate. Most of her jokes were at other people's expense, and she made her mark laughing at others' misfortunes rather than directing her humorous remarks at herself. People do not, on the whole, enjoy being the butt of jokes and sarcasm. It makes them feel uneasy and uncomfortable. Hurtfully sarcastic people who are always trying to put others down eventually find themselves without an audience. But more than that, hostile humour directed at other people only increases a feeling of hatred and alienation in the humorist.

Dorothy Parker, in her public utterances at least, could hardly make a kindly remark. Her book reviews were as cruel as her spoken wit. One example will give the idea. When reviewing A.A. Milne's *House at Pooh Corner* for her 'Constant Reader' column, she wrote simply: 'Tonstant weader frowed up.' This kind of remark is not conducive to any kind of good feeling, though it is clever.

A CURE FOR POMPOSITY

People who have an exaggerated sense of their own importance and take themselves far too seriously ask to be made fun of, and often are. Public figures such as politicians, moral rights campaigners, chairmen of large corporations and top civil servants are very often the butt of other people's humour. The humour arises out of the gap between the pomposity of the public figure and the situation that person is put in by the satirist. We laugh when public people are ridiculed because when they are being serious, they try to make us afraid of them. We can become nervous of their power, and when they are ridiculed they are cut down to size and seen to be not so fearsome after all.

'Amusement and laughter,' says Branko Bokun in his pioneering book, *Humour Therapy*, 'are the result of victory over fear ... Humour is a realistic vision or perception of the world around us.' There is a potent difference between wit and humour. Whereas humour is always positive, wit can be extremely destructive — often vindictive and malicious, directed at others in order to increase their discomfiture, and put the perpetrator in a position of power. People tend to feel superior when they are being witty, and there is usually at least some degree of hostility in the verbal attack. And, as Brando Bokun points out, most wits would far prefer to lose a friend than the opportunity of making a witty remark.

One can see this phenomenon at work in the fluctuating fortunes of the satirical magazine *Private Eye*. Though its columns and stories are often very funny, they are almost always written with the aim of doing somebody down, of being negative. Though, for more than two decades, the magazine has entertained us by poking fun at the pompous and the egotistical, the wit is usually cruel. The net result is that the contributors and editors are always falling out with each other, and huge libel actions threaten continuously. The other aspect is that, however much the self-inflated figures are lampooned in *Private Eye*, they tend to march on unscathed, as little interrupted by the savage satire as by an annoying fly. They simply swat it away and discount it.

Though magazines like *Private Eye* attempt to cut the self-important down to size, they rarely succeed. However much others may draw attention to foibles and ridiculous behaviour, it will not alter the individuals criticised. They will not mend their ways unless they see for themselves that their behaviour has been wrong. By contrast, people who have a well developed sense of humour seldom become pompous. As a result, they are less likely to harm themselves or other people.

People who have no sense of humour have simply no idea of how ridiculous or inappropriate their behaviour may seem to others. They have no notion of the impact they may be making, and little sensitivity to the thoughts and impressions of others. They are concerned only with themselves. Having a sense of humour means that a person is able to make constant checks on behaviour, so that nothing ever gets too far out of hand.

As men seem more prone than women to reach ridiculous heights of ego, it is correspondingly more important for them to develop a sense of humour. Women tend more to suffer from the opposite problem: they can become cowed, passive and nervous. Both an inflated ego and extreme passivity have the same root cause: fear. Developing a sense of humour would enable many fearful

women to start laughing at themselves, and thus become more courageous and assertive. The quality is very much needed by both sexes. Yet in our present society, it is often in short supply.

DEVELOPING A SENSE OF HUMOUR

Branko Bokun analyses the importance of a sense of humour thus: as babies and children, he says, we are all born with a predisposition towards playfulness. Toddlers and small children naturally want to play, and will take any opportunity to do so. They love laughter and fun. Children are happiest when they are laughing, and there are few sights more pleasing to an adult than that of children happily at play, taking delight from the simple enjoyment of life.

With adolescence, however, both boys and girls tend to start taking themselves too seriusly. Playful expressions, which were natural in childhood, give way to moodiness and sulkiness. I remember as a teenager myself that I would never, if possible, smile for photographers. I thought that smiling made me look daft and childish. It seemed more grown-up to be serious. Today's teenagers are exactly the same, and hardly ever smile if they can help it. Those who reckon they are 'cool' and stylish smile as little as they possibly can. Almost all magazines aimed at the teenage market show adolescents looking moody, and with glowering eyes.

It is during the teenage years that it becomes vital to develop a sense of humour. Children don't need humour so much — they laugh at things easily. But if we forget to laugh and smile as teenagers, and in particular to laugh at ourselves, we risk getting into the habit of being too serious as adults. And that increases the danger of stress building up and not finding an outlet.

All stress, Bokun says, arises from fear of some kind, and humour is the only thing that can dispel it. As soon as we become adolescent, we tend to start taking ourselves far too seriously, and this new attitude is reflected in our faces and in our posture. Instead of being flexible and relaxed, the face and body become ever more rigid and set. Those who lose the ability to laugh easily can become intolerant of others, narrow-minded and rigid in their mental attitudes.

OVERSERIOUSNESS

One of the most damaging mental attributes anybody can have is a hermetically sealed mind, one which is closed to any new ideas or impressions. It is damaging because it leads to increased fear, and this in turn causes stress, which in the end results in ill-health.

Novelists often depict intensely serious, narrow-minded individuals who think they are more important than they are. They are never sympathetic people. One of the most famous examples of a totally humourless, uninspired, cold and rigid fictional character is the clergyman Edward Casaubon in George Eliot's *Middlemarch*. He was so convinced of the seriousness and importance of his life's work, *The Key to All Mythologies*, that everything else took second place. His young wife Dorothea, who had the romantic notion of helping him, soon became disillusioned and realized she had paid dearly for marrying a dream. *The Key to All Mythologies*, she soon learned, was rubbish and it never would be finished. Moreover, her husband knew inwardly that it was rubbish, and this was the deep-seated reason why he could never complete it.

Playwright Alan Ayckbourn invented a similar character — again, a vicar — for his hit play *A Woman in Mind*. Here the heroine, a middle-aged clergyman's wife, was slowly being driven mad by the pomposity and stupidity of her husband. He, too, was engaged on his life's work — a history of the local parish.

These two fictional characters provide examples of how overseriousness can lead to silliness and prejudice, and reveal an unexpected lack of intelligence. Those who have no sense of humour risk cutting themselves off from the feedback others provide, and which would give them a realistic attitude to themselves and to any work they may be engaged on. Any work undertaken without a sense of humour is unlikely to add to the sum of the world's happiness. There is always humour in Shakespeare, even in his darkest plays, which is one reason they are always enjoyable. The serious, striving characters in the plays are always being laughed at by others, so that we, as the audience, can perceive the gap between what they really are and what they pretend to be.

Humour is vital in our society because it closes the gap between perception and reality. This is the view of psychiatrist Hans Eysenck, formerly a professor at the Institute of Psychiatry. Humour offers a bridge between what ought to be and what is. In our current society we need humour more than ever before, we need to know that much of what we do is inherently ridiculous. When we acknowledge this, things do not become more ridiculous, but less so.

FREUD ON HUMOUR

In his book *Jokes and Their Relation to the Unconscious*, Freud explains what he understands by humour. The book is, unfortunately, one of the most unfunny pieces of writing ever penned, and leaves one wondering whether Freud himself had any sense of humour at all. Even so, it has become a classic work on the subject, and offers useful working definitions. Jokes, says Freud, are primarily intended to give pleasure, to bring out something that was previously hidden or unacknowledged. Freud defines two distinct types of joke — the innocent, which may be merely a play on words, and the tendentious, which has a more sinister origin. With pleasurable jokes, he says, there is a clear sense of satisfaction, a slight smile, and a temporary lightening of the atmosphere. Everybody feels a bit happier when an innocent joke is cracked, even if it is not wildly funny.

Jokes cease to become innocent, and fall into the tendentious category, when the motivation behind them is hostile or obscene. The hostile joke is one where the perpetrator has an aggressive, satirical or defensive motive, and the obscene joke serves to expose something which normally remains hidden and out of sight. Freud defines 'smut' as being when sexual facts and relationships are intentionally brought into prominence by speech. A lecture on anatomy or reproduction would not normally be amusing or smutty, says Freud.

Sexual allusions turn into blue jokes when they emphasize attitudes that people would normally wish to hide. The purpose of smut, according to Freud, is to increase sexual excitement or arousal in the minds of the hearers by reminding them of sexual parts and sexual acts. Freud concludes that all smut is fundamentally directed at women, as some kind of crass seduction technique. It is actually, he writes, an act of sexual aggression masked as humour. As such, smut cannot be considered genuinely funny at all.

Freud believes that obscene jokes exist only in repressed societies. If we were all open and honest about sex, he says, there would be no room for obscene jokes. Because sexual matters would no longer be hidden, there would be no reason to allude to them in indirect ways. If we were less repressed, *double entendres* would cease to be funny. Many decades have passed since Freud wrote his book and we are supposed now to be less repressed, yet smutty humour is as popular as ever. Books of crude jokes still sell by the millions. Here are some typical examples of what are commonly referred to as 'rugby' jokes:

They're washing off all those dirty jokes

Arriving home unexpectedly from a business trip, the husband found his wife in bed with his best friend, in what may be described as a compromising position.

'Look here,' shouted the husband. 'Just what do you think you're doing?'

'SEE!' said the wife to the man beside her. 'Didn't I tell you he was stupid?'

A young couple travelled by train to their honeymoon hotel. During the journey the woman fondled her man under the cover of a newspaper spread across his lap. Later they both dozed off and a breeze blew the newspaper onto the floor.

Then the conductor came by. 'Wake up Madam,' he said. 'Your bouquet has wilted.'

Three sisters were preparing to go out for the evening. All three went to say goodbye to their mother before they left.

'I'm going out with Pete to eat,' said the first.

'That's nice, darling,' said the mother. 'Try not to be late.'

'I'm going out with Lance to dance,' said the second.

'How lovely!' said the mother. 'But do keep an eye on the time.'

'I'm going out with Chuck,' said the third.

'Oh no you're not,' said the mother. 'You're staying right here.'

In recent years, there has been much more openness about sex than ever before, yet people still find jokes with sexual allusions among the funniest. There is a great deal of humour about sex because we know so much of it is inherently ridiculous. We may be ashamed of certain acts and of certain parts of the body, but we are also ashamed of being ashamed. As it is all supposed to be 'natural', we try to make it so by cracking jokes. Sexual jokes which are not smutty, hostile or aggressive do serve a therapeutic purpose, as they stop the subject from becoming overladen with inappropriate seriousness or pomposity.

Pornography is never humorous, but always deadly serious. Once humour enters in, the fantasy ends. And pornography is essentially fantasy.

In his book, Freud also discusses hostile humour. He defines this as a kind of displacement. Polite society, he writes, does not allow us to be as hostile to others as we would sometimes like. We usually have to cover up our aggression with a veneer of politeness, so we displace inner hostility and transform it into verbal hostility. Somehow this evens things up.

Hostile humour finds a particular expression in feminist jokes. 'If they can put a man on the moon,' went one piece of graffiti, 'why can't they put them all there?' Defacing advertisements has become a popular feminist activity. Underneath a car advertisement saying: 'To Volvo, a son', were scrawled the words: 'Better luck next time.' On a tights advertisement with the slogan: 'Where would we be without pins?' someone wrote: 'Free from little pricks.' A favourite piece of feminist graffiti goes: 'They say marriage is a bed of roses, but beware of the pricks.'

'By making an enemy small, inferior, despicable or comic, we achieve in a roundabout way the enjoyment of overcoming him,' Freud states. 'The joke allows us to exploit something ridiculous in our enemy which we could not bring forward deliberately or openly.' The pleasure in such a joke comes from satisfying an instinct which would otherwise be repressed. We could be angry, but the joke makes us laugh instead.

Jokes also serve to deflect criticism away from the person who is making the joke. As most witty people realize, the best way to stop people from laughing at you is to laugh at yourself first. This gives potent protection and provides you with a mental suit of armour that others are unable to penetrate. It is often said of very witty people, or of people who are always making jokes, that you can't get through to them. By this it is meant that you can't get to their sensitive points. Because they tend to make a joke out of everything, they seem to have no vulnerability. Those who are always making jokes against themselves, or who can successfully deflect potentially wounding remarks, are never teased or made fun of. You can always only tease the teasable, and the teasable people are ones who get upset easily.

Having a sense of humour stops people from being oversensitive, and imagining that every personal remark is meant to hurt or wound. Those who can laugh at themselves are never the butt of other people's humour. There is just no fun in trying to make a joke about someone's big nose, height or glasses, if the victim of the would-be joke gets in first every time.

Most jokes, if they are good ones, end in laughter, which acts as a release from constraint and uptightness. 'Laughter arises,' says Freud, 'when free discharge becomes possible.' Laughter is a lifting of inhibitions and repressions, a casting off of the heavy cloak of conformism and seriousness which always threatens to engulf our lives.

We need humour, concludes Freud, because as we grow up, we are liable to become very unhappy people. Children laugh easily. As we get older, it is increasingly difficult for us to see the funny side of things. We become enmeshed in jobs, marriage, mortgages, insurance, and all the other

trappings of adulthood, and life often loses its joy. We badly need jokes to put us back in touch with that essential part of ourselves that can laugh and smile and be carefree. 'Humour,' writes Freud, 'is a means of obtaining pleasure in spite of distressing happenings and circumstances.' Humour is a necessary safety valve because so much of adult life is emphatically not happy and lighthearted.

Adults do things with the object of enjoying themselves, but often the enjoyment is absent. We try to have fun, but can't. If we were happy most of the time it would not be so essential to have a sense of humour. But as things are, the very best way of reviving a sense of pleasure in life is to laugh at the situations that cause distress.

Humour is vital because it stops us worrying too much about things. It is often the case that we either laugh at something, or let it bother us. Once we are able to laugh, the bother and worry go, and the problem fades into insignificance. Freud does not discuss the relationship between humour and health, but he does believe that it is not possible to be mentally happy without having a sense of humour, and using it wherever possible.

A sense of humour is a wholly positive resource and is there, or should be, in reserve to brighten up every potentially dreary corner of life. Humour enables us to retain pleasure in life, a pleasure that is always in danger of being lost.

4.
SMILE THERAPY: HOW IT WORKS

When we are happy, we naturally smile and laugh a lot.
We don't consciously have to make ourselves look and feel
cheerful. When we are in a good mood, our facial
expressions naturally reflect our high spirits. When we feel
miserable, we equally naturally look miserable and
downcast.

As our emotions are so accurately reflected on our faces,
it has long been assumed that facial expressions follow on
after the emotion has been felt. That is to say, you first
feel happy, or miserable — and the appropriate facial
expression will then display itself.

But, from recent research into the subject, it seems
equally likely that if you force a particular expression onto
your face, then your mind and body will respond, and will
biochemically register that emotion. If you are feeling
unhappy for some reason, and are asked to smile, your
new, happy expression will actually make you feel better
inside, as it will affect the hormones coursing through your
system.

This idea clearly has great potential in the healing field.
When people feel ill, or are in great pain, it usually
manifests itself in an expression of misery or agony. But if
the miserable expression can be replaced by a cheerful one
— even though the illness or pain may still be present —
the healing process can actually be set in motion.

FIRST EXPRESSION, THEN EMOTION?

It may sound a peculiar idea, but this theory has been scientifically demonstrated by US scientists. Paul Ekman is at the forefront of research in this field, and another psychologist, Robert Zajonc, of Ann Arbor, University of Michigan, has also carried out studies to discover which comes first: expression or emotion.

Zajonc's research harks back to some studies undertaken at the beginning of the century. In a paper entitled *Emotional and Facial Efference: A Theory Reclaimed*, Zajonc refers to a long-forgotten book by French physiologist Israel Waynbaum called *Physionomie Humaine; Son Méchanisme et son Rôle Social*, published in 1906. Waynbaum believed that the facial muscles act as ligatures on the blood vessels and regulate blood flow to the brain. The blood flow in turn influences how we feel. The theory he developed held that emotions often follow on from facial expressions, rather than always preceding them.

Waynbaum hypothesized that all overt emotional responses, such as blushing, sobbing, weeping and so on are closely tied to vascular processes. Weeping and laughter affect the blood circulation, in particular via the actions of the diaphragm. Waynbaum argued that all emotional reactions affect the circulation, whether positively or negatively, and that facial expressions play an important part in this process.

Why is it, Waynbaum asked, that smiling and laughter are always associated with happiness and joy? He postulated that increased blood flow to the brain — which is the physiological result of smiling and laughter — is associated with a healthy body and a positive mood. Depressive moods and expressions, by contrast, result in a decreased flow of blood to the brain. This in time can lead to actual physical ill health. So people who constantly go around with gloomy expressions on their faces are causing a permanent decrease of blood to the brain. This means that the brain is not receiving proper nutrients, and is not working at optimum levels.

Waynbaum reports noticing that, when people make themselves smile, they often feel happier. It is obviously better to do this than to wait until you feel happy in order to smile. We all know that we can come home from a hard and frustrating day at work, switch on the television to watch a top comedy show, and have our mood lifted within minutes. Nothing will have happened to change our mood internally — the circumstances that caused the frustrations will still be there — but we are able to forget our worries by losing ourselves in smiling and laughter. According to Waynbaum's theory, the mere acts of smiling and laughing increase the blood flow to the brain, and it is this which serves to improve our mood.

When a person laughs helplessly, the increased circulation may result in a form of congestion which can become acutely painful, and cause what we call a stitch. However, by this time the individual's mood has improved so much that this discomfort is not perceived as pain, but is in itself a perversely enjoyable side effect. Laughter often results in tears, as these serve to relieve the rising pressure of cerebral blood, and normalize it when the congestion threatens to become too great. As laughter is a safety valve, so tears provide an extra safety valve when

we are overcome with laughter. Tears stop the laughter from being too much of a good thing.

The zygomatic muscle is most associated with smiling and happiness. This muscle, according to Waynbaum's theory, directly causes more blood to flow round the brain. Veins become engorged with blood, and this in itself actually lightens moods and makes people happy.

In his book Waynbaum puts forward the idea that laughing must be a healthy activity because improved circulation is a good thing. Laughing is rather like taking an oxygen bath — the cells and tissues all receive an increased supply of oxygen and this results in a feeling of exuberance. What happens inside is that thin, depleted blood in the veins is converted into oxygen-filled arterial blood, and the lungs are then oxygenated at a more rapid rate. But feeling and looking sad results in dysoxygenation of the blood, and deprives the cells of oxygen. They become starved and depleted, and the result is depression, anxiety and misery.

Happiness, Waynbaum concludes, is the best elixir of youth we have, since smiling involves only the one muscle, whereas in order to look sad many muscles have to be contracted and contorted. If a sad expression becomes permanent, wrinkles will result. You simply cannot develop as many wrinkles from smiling and looking happy.

A CURE FOR MENTAL ILLNESS?

Commenting on the Waynbaum theory, Zajonc points out that we know that arterial blood has the effect of cooling down the brain. It could well be that brain temperature influences neurotransmitters, the hormones that convey emotional states and feelings to all parts of the body. It also seems likely that when we are miserable, and blood flow to the brain is inhibited, this impairs the release and synthesis of important neurotransmitters.

When the brain is well supplied with highly oxygenated blood it is likely to work better than when it is starved of it. Illness is, above all, a result of disharmony in the body. It seems more than reasonable to suggest that we would be liable to feel miserable and ill if the amount of blood going to the brain meant that the brain could not work optimally.

The brain remembers things for a very long time and it is unlikely that it ever completely forgets anything thoroughly experienced. So, if you attempt to smile when you are feeling sad, the brain will remember that this expression has in the past been associated with feeling happy, and will immediately start to respond by releasing the appropriate neurotransmitters. The result, says Zajonc, is that a happier and more positive state will be induced.

Zajonc feels that Waynbaum's idea could be of great help in treating patients with psychosomatic disorders, and negative conditions such as depression and anxiety. If anxious and depressed patients could be taught to control the appropriate facial muscles so that they looked happy

instead of sad, they could well discover that they actually
started to feel better, without anything else having
changed.

Certainly, nobody would say that current treatment of
mental patients is an unqualified success, and some
psychologists would call it a signal failure. Yet doctors
have been reluctant to try smile therapy — perhaps
because it sounds unscientific, does not take seven years'
training, and costs no money. It sounds too simple and
ordinary to be effective. Most of the drug treatments
currently given to mental patients shut down their body
processes. The so-called anti-depressants and major
tranquillizers given to patients in psychiatric hospitals
actually make them more depressed: they serve only to
cut off certain signals to the brain, so patients are less
bothered by their depression. They become zombie-like,
not cured. Smile therapy could actually do far more good,
by increasing blood flow to the brain and causing release
of the neurotransmitters associated with positive states.

So smile therapy would be a natural way of overcoming
mental pain and distress. Though it cannot be guaranteed
to work in every case, and its success would depend on the
length of time the suffering had lasted and the depth of
the misery — at the very least, smiling would cheer people
up and give a temporary respite from woe. Robert
Zajonc's conclusion is that all mental patients, and many
suffering from physical complaints, should be taught to
smile as a practical part of their therapy.

MAKE YOURSELF FEEL HAPPY

Paul Ekman has demonstrated more or less conclusively
that if you force yourself to smile, or indeed to simulate
any emotion by adopting the appropriate facial
expression, that emotion will soon be felt in the brain and
body. His pioneering work has been written up in various
US scientific journals, and sheds important light on the
efficacy of smiling as valuable therapy.

Ekman began his research by asking the question: Does

the activity of the autonomic nervous system, or ANS (which is beyond conscious control and works automatically) differ with each specific emotion? As long ago as 1890 the psychologist William James had suggested that each emotion had a demonstrably different pattern of ANS activity. Ekman and his co-workers at the University of California decided to put this idea to the test, and for their experiments persuaded a series of volunteers, including a number of actors, to simulate various expressions and emotions.

Ekman studied six 'pure' emotions — surprise, sadness, anger, fear, disgust and happiness. As the emotions were portrayed on the faces of his guinea pigs, instruments recorded differences in heart rate, temperature, muscle tension and skin resistance. In the first experiment, the volunteers were asked to contract specific muscles. Then they were asked to remember and record on their faces the emotions under investigation. The expressions were each held for 10 seconds.

Even though there was no indication that the subjects actually experienced any emotion, they did undergo dramatic bodily changes. Negative emotions showed a marked increase in ANS activity. All of the emotions under investigation, with the exception of happiness were, of course, negative. It was found that heart rate increased far more when anger was being simulated than when the subjects were asked to look happy, and also that finger temperature went up for anger but not for happiness. Throughout, anger showed greater increases in ANS activity than any of the other negative emotions such as surprise, disgust or sadness.

This laboratory experiment shows that all the body's systems become involuntarily hyped up and on 'red alert' during simulation of negative emotions, but are calmed down when positive emotions are simulated by the appropriate facial expression. Ekman concludes that there is a direct and central connection between the muscle action and the centres of the brain. This leads him to wonder, along with Robert Zajonc, whether voluntary

facial actions could be used therapeutically. If somebody is anxious, he says, then deliberately realigning the facial muscles into a non-anxious expression could actually alter the hormonal pathways associated with conveying emotions. If anxious and depressed people are asked to redirect their facial expressions, this alone could relieve their depression.

Similarly, going to a social gathering where smiling politely is the only acceptable form of behaviour may actually turn out to be enjoyable, whatever storms may be raging inside. So often, people decline social invitations because they say they are just not in the mood. But that could in fact be the strongest reason for going to an occasion that demands a smile and lighthearted behaviour. If you forced yourself to smile all evening, you could come away feeling far better than before because of the positive hormones now coursing round your system.

However strongly felt the emotion, an accompanying facial expression can only be held for four seconds at the most. If it is maintained for longer than that, the muscles can start going into spasm. But it appears that the ANS changes — for better or for worse — last far longer than the facial expression. However, they may not last for hours, so if body systems are to be kept calm and harmonious, you have to keep finding things to smile about.

As with anything else, facial expressions can become a habit. It is possible to be a habitual smiler and laugher. Whether your facial expression mirrors your internal emotions or not, the ANS activity will be the same. So somebody whose face is permanently set in anger — even though they may not be feeling especially angry all the time — will nevertheless have raised heart rate and skin temperature, and all the other activities associated with increased stress in the system. To look happy and to laugh a lot signals to the body that you are not afraid, and feel calm and peaceful. The body will respond positively even when you are just pretending to be cheerful and happy.

THE POSITIVE EFFECTS OF SMILING

New scientific research shows that the old music-hall injunction to 'pack up your troubles in your old kit-bag and smile, smile, smile' has a fundamental validity. Happiness is not just in the mind, but is embodied in our muscles and hormones. The act of putting facial muscles into the expressions associated with joy can produce far-reaching positive effects on the nervous systems.

Paul Ekman, the chief researcher in this field, believes that the mechanics of facial muscle movement are intimately connected to the autonomic nervous system, which controls heart rate, breathing and other functions beyond conscious control.

The act of smiling, and of smiling when you don't feel like it, can also affect the spirits and the ANS activity of people around you. Research indicates that people tend to mimic the expressions of others. If somebody greets you at the door with a smile, you will tend to smile back. If they scowl and look unhappy, then you may mimic this expression instead.

We all, often consciously, pick up the moods of those we live with, and imitate them. If your partner is cross, you often feel cross yourself. This means that we have a duty to look happy as often as possible, so that we can heal ourselves and also act as healers of other people. One reason why we all enjoy comedy shows so much, according to Paul Ekman, is that the smiling faces of the comedians affect the activity of our own autonomic nervous systems, as well as theirs. When we perceive expressions on other people's faces, we are not just receiving information, but actually experiencing with them the emotions they are feeling. This could have important consequences for the treatment of psychiatric patients, and indeed, for our whole approach to illness. Ekman believes that his discoveries confirm truths that were known long ago, but which our high-tech age has forgotten.

Great writers have always known the power of facial expressions. In Edgar Allan Poe's *Purloined Letter*, he writes that when he wants to discover how wise, stupid, good or evil a person is, or what he is thinking at that moment, he puts his own face into the expression he can see on the other person. 'I fashion the expression of my face, as accurately as possible, in accordance with the expression of his, and then wait to see what thoughts or sentiments arise in my mind or heart.' Poe of course, could know nothing of hormonal or chemical pathways, or ANS activity, but he hit intuitively on the truth.

The medical profession could take heed of these findings by making sure that hospitals, surgeries and health centres were jollier places. It is true that some attempts are being made to enliven children's wards, which are now very often painted in bright colours and with cheerful pictures round the walls. The paradox is that children need this brightening up so much less than adults as their disposition is naturally more cheerful, even when they are ill.

Adult wards, however, desperately need brightening up. Doctors and nurses could benefit by taking lessons in smiling and laughter, and their courses could underline the importance of keeping cheerful — the more serious the illness, the more vital is a cheerful expression. We have, unfortunately, come to associate gravity of expression with intelligence and authority, and assume that the doctor's stern face means that she or he must know what is best. In fact, showing disgust, anger or sadness only serves to increase the patient's fear and alienation. Gloomy faces actually spread fear, and fear stops people from regaining their health.

In ordinary social life, we can do a lot to prevent ourselves from becoming ill by remembering to smile whenever possible. Many behavioural problems could, according to Ekman, be averted if people were persuaded of the importance of smiling. It would be less easy to become caught in a vicious, downward cycle of depression and despair if facial expressions were kept positive. People imagine this is difficult to do, but in fact it is not. Once it is understood that facial expressions really do affect emotions, smile therapy can be put into practice.

5.
WHY LAUGHTER IS THE BEST MEDICINE

THE CASE OF NORMAN COUSINS

The idea that laughter could actually be used as an effective means of therapy was first tried out by Norman Cousins, an American journalist who developed a distressing condition known as ankylosing spondylitis, where the spine becomes increasingly immobile, and the patient is gradually crippled. The condition is considered incurable and can be excrutiatingly painful.

Cousins, a former editor of the US *Saturday Review*, contracted the illness in 1964. He soon discovered that being in hospital worsened his condition, rather than improving it. As he lay there, he began to wonder whether there could be any connection between positive emotions and getting better — he knew that there was a direct link between negative emotions and certain illnesses. Since none of his other treatments were working, he decided to give it a try. In his account of the process, *Anatomy of an Illness, as Perceived by the Patient,* he writes: 'We began calling for the full exercise of the affirmative emotions as a factor in enhancing body chemistry. It was easy enough to hope and love and have faith, but what about laughter? Nothing is less funny than being flat on your back, with all the bones in your back and joints hurting.'

Instead of continuing with the strong painkilling drugs prescribed by his doctors, Cousins moved out of the hospital into a hotel room, there to carry on his own treatment. After all, he reasoned, he had nothing whatever to lose. His hotel room was one-third the cost of his American hospital room — a fact Cousins found cheering in itself — and was more 'therapeutic' in that it was not so closely associated with illness. Once installed, he hired dozens of Marx Brothers and Candid Camera films, and sat down to watch them. He then discovered that every time he laughed, the laughter acted as an anaesthetic and gave him relief from pain. At the same time as taking the laughter cure, Cousins was swallowing massive doses — what we should now call megadoses — of vitamin C. This unlikely but happy combination really did work.

Not all his infirmities disappeared overnight, but the cycle of fear, depression and panic in which he had become trapped slowly began to reverse. He found that laughter was definitely able to reduce the inflammation in his joints, and felt certain that laughing was actually stimulating the production of endorphins — natural painkillers — in the brain. Laughter in itself seemed to create a mood in which other positive emotions could be put to work. He took the vitamin C in such large doses because he had read in various medical journals that ascorbic acid helped to oxygenate the blood. If inadequate oxygen was a factor in collagen breakdown, which precipitated his disease, couldn't vitamin C help reverse the process?

Cousins wrote:

> How scientific was it to believe that laughter — as well as the positive emotions in general — was affecting my body chemistry for the better? If laughter did in fact have a salutary effect on the body's chemistry, it seemed at least theoretically likely that it would enhance the system's ability to fight the inflammation.
>
> So we took sedimentation rate readings just before as well as several hours after the laughter episodes. [Cousins had

found a doctor, William Hitzig, who was prepared to go along with his theory, and try it out.] Each time there was a drop of at least five points. Each by itself was not substantial, but it held and was cumulative. I was greatly elated by the discovery that there is a physiological basis for the ancient theory that laughter is good medicine.

After a few weeks of the laughter cure, Cousins discovered that the combination really was working: whatever had been eating away at his connective tissue was no longer making progress.

Seldom had I known such elation. The ascorbic acid was working. So was laughter. The combination was cutting heavily into whatever poison was attacking the connective tissue. The fever was receding and the pulse was no longer racing.

We stepped up the dosage. On the second day we went to 12.5 grams of ascorbic acid, on the third day, 15 grams and so on until the end of the week, when we reached 25 grams. Meanwhile, the laughter routine was in full force. I was completely off drugs and sleeping pills. Sleep — blessed, natural sleep without pain — was becoming increasingly prolonged ...

I must not make it appear that all my infirmities disappeared overnight. For many months I couldn't get my arms up far enough to reach for a book on a high shelf. My fingers weren't agile enough to do what I wanted them to do on the organ keyboard. My neck had a limited turning radius. My knees were somewhat wobbly, and off and on, I have had to wear a metal brace.

Even so, I was sufficiently recovered to go back to my job at the *Saturday Review* full-time again, and this was miracle enough for me.

Cousins' account of his recovery is interspersed with the notion that hospitals are not suitable places for seriously ill people. Not only is laughter noticeably absent, the routines and treatments seem actually designed to make people more ill than they were before. In his book Cousins speaks of the lack of respect for basic sanitation, the indiscriminate use of X-rays and electronic equipment, the way in which powerful drugs are handed out routinely, and the impossibility of getting a good night's sleep. The hotel he moved into, by contrast, was a place where recovery was far easier. There he was not wakened for a bed bath or for meals, for tests or for medication. 'The serenity,' he wrote, 'was delicious and would, I felt certain, contribute to a general improvement.'

Norman Cousins monitored his laughter cure very precisely, and discovered that 10 minutes of genuine belly laughter could provide an anaesthetic effect which lasted for at least two hours. When the pain-killing effect of the laughter wore off, he would start the projector rolling again and watch more funny films. 'Not infrequently,' he wrote, 'it would lead to another pain-free sleep interval. Sometimes the nurse read me a trove of humor books.' Among those that produced the desired effect were E.B. and Katharine White's *Subtreasury of American Humor* and Max Eastman's *The Enjoyment of Laughter*.

THE MEDICAL REACTION

When Norman Cousins' book was published in 1978, long after he had made a complete recovery from his condition, it created a furore of disbelief within the medical profession. There was no doubt that Cousins had recovered — he had been crippled and now he could walk — but was it *really* due to the laughter? It seemed a pretty far-fetched notion. If, as he alleged, laughter could cure serious conditions, why was it not emphasized more in medical schools?

It seemed to the majority of doctors that the intervals of no pain Cousins had gained from laughing at Marx Brothers films could not possibly be curative. Also, they asked, could vitamin C genuinely have aided a cure? Was it real, or was it, as most doctors preferred to believe, simply a placebo effect, whereby something will cure if you believe in it enough? The consensus of opinion was that, though laughing at Candid Camera films may have helped Cousins, there was no evidence to suggest that this treatment could help anybody else suffering from the same condition. So Cousins' case, far from radically changing the attitude of the medical profession, simply became a medical curiosity, and his book is now out of print.

The idea, however, once implanted, refused to go away. Though so many doctors poured scorn on Cousins' theories and ideas — he wasn't, after all, a doctor himself, so how could he know anything? — lay people who were looking after patients suffering from serious illnesses began to wonder if there wasn't something in what was being said. And now doctors themselves are starting to come round to the idea that positive emotions can help people where conventional treatments may have failed.

The work of Paul Ekman and others has helped the medical profession to see smiling and laughter in a new and more therapeutic light. Some time after the publication of Cousins' story (it first saw the light of day in the prestigious medical publication, *The New England Journal of Medicine,* and was only later expanded into a book) he was offered an associate professorship at the School of Medicine, University of California. Cousins, now in his 70s, continues to preach the efficacy of laughter as a healing tool, and doctors are now at last beginning to take the idea seriously.

A paper published in the British *Journal of the Royal College of General Practitioners* in August 1985 stated categorically that laughter was medically good for people. 'Laughing affects every organ in the body,' the editorial stated, 'and the bigger the belly laugh, the better it is for us. When we laugh we secrete hormones that stimulate the heart and act as natural painkillers. Stress is reduced. Calories are burned off and digestion is improved.' So there you are — laughter now has the sanction of that august and conservative body, the Royal College of General Practitioners.

You can, they say, literally laugh off fat because the act of laughing increases metabolic rate. What happens when we laugh is that the circulation and digestive processes are improved and the whole system becomes far less sluggish. The ability of laughter to get the system moving again provided a cure for Norman Cousins.

An article in the medical journal *The Practitioner*, by British consultant pathologist A.R. Kittermaster, also praises the therapeutic value of laughter. Speaking of the 'laughter cure', he writes:

> The human animal is poised, in its anxiety, to blow itself to bits by global war. Seen from a distance, mankind must look like a mass of demented ants, rushing hither and thither destroying themselves by their anxieties, and gathering in groups to plot total destruction for all, out of fear that one group might otherwise get the upper hand.
>
> Come on, homo not-so-sapiens, before it is too late we must stop behaving like a bunch of frightened adolescents and learn to laugh at ourselves and our twisted animal instincts. Laughter at self is lethal to pathological anxiety. For those who can laugh happily at themselves, all stress diseases will evaporate overnight.

LAUGHTER AGAINST STRESS

Other doctors too, have started to extol the potent benefits of laughter. Dr Joan Gomez, a London psychiatrist, writes in the magazine *Good Health* that laughter is by far the best way of coping with stress and stress-related conditions: 'Stress is just part of everyday living for most of us. But there are ways of coping with it successfully. One of the best medicines is laughter. Laughter melts away stress like ice under a blow lamp.'

Dr Gomez goes on to define stress as a challenge to the system which is not successfully overcome. When you deal with stress, she says, the challenge becomes an achievement. But when you feel threatened and under siege, stress starts to attack the body. Many things can cause stress — physical pain, emotional suffering or mental anguish. Boredom and lack of purpose, loneliness and bereavement are all potential causes of stress, as is fear of personal failure. Fears and conflict cause the most stress and before long they manifest themselves as actual physical conditions.

Even minor stress can cause tension, fatigue, restlessness, irritability and insomnia. There may be headaches, backaches or stomach ulcers, indigestion or an awareness of the heart thumping. If the stress continues, there is a likelihood of real illness developing. Angina, high blood pressure, coughs, colds and flu may all be caused or made worse by stress.

The way to cure stress is not to take pills to mask the anxiety, but to understand the problem and deal with it. And laugh, of course. You do not need necessarily to laugh at the problem causing the stress; any laughter, whatever its cause, can have a beneficial effect. Dr Gomez says: 'Half an hour of Les Dawson may be all you need to make your tension disappear.'

The article goes on to explain exactly what laughter is. Laughing, like weeping, is a respiratory exercise made up of a sequence of quick, deep breaths released spasmodically through part-closed vocal chords. Face, shoulder, trunk and chest muscles and diaphragm are all involved. When we laugh, we release tears, relax blood vessels which are near the skin, and reduce blood pressure. Laughter is a muscle relaxant, and makes us feel weak rather than ready for action. Stress has the effect of hyping up the body systems, making us ready for action, even when no action is required or suitable.

Over the past few years, since stress was acknowledged to be the West's number one killer, many forms of relaxation have been recommended. People under stress have been told to try meditation, yoga or exercise. The problem with these is that they don't suit everybody.

Not everybody benefits from taking exercise either. Many thousands have taken up jogging, expecting to find it relaxing, and have been disappointed. Aerobic and other indoor exercises can have a far from relaxing effect. But laughter benefits everybody — it is actually impossible not to enjoy laughing, and impossible not to benefit from it.

Laughter is a more rapid, surer and more effective way of inducing bodily relaxation than meditation, exercises or pills. Emotionally, laughter has a similar effect to having a good cry, except that laughter is better for you. Both crying and laughter help to release tensions and feelings without the use of words, which can often add to the stress.

Laughter, concludes Dr Gomez in her article, is essentially a shared activity. It is only the mentally disturbed who laugh alone and without any obvious stimulus, such as a funny book or television show. Laughter is good for humans because it implies safety. We do not laugh when we are afraid, and so when we laugh we cannot continue to be fearful. Though people can put on false smiles, it is almost impossible to laugh without meaning it. When you laugh, all your controls are off, and you have no choice but to give yourself over to the enjoyment of the moment. 'There is no pretence, no deception, no danger,' says Dr Gomez.

LAUGHING AND CANCER

Apart from its value in keeping people healthy and free from stress, laughter is now being used in some hospitals as a healing tool for serious diseases such as cancer. Most of the pioneering work for this has been carried out in the United States, where certain hospitals now have 'laughter rooms' where patients can try the Norman Cousins cure. Deborah Leiberm, founder of the association Nurses for Laughter, says: 'For 60 to 80 years we have been looking at negative emotions — depression, hostility, anger — and their effects on health. Now it is time to look at the flip side.'

Dr Carl Simonton and his wife Stephanie Matthews Simonton, both cancer experts, also believe in the value of smiling and laughter in the reversal of cancerous growths. One researcher, Dr Janet S. Hranicky, who has been working with the Simontons for over seven years, has developed a theory about cancer which she calls the 'pleasure freeze'. When people have cancer, or may be prone to develop cancer, it is noticeable that they lose their ability to laugh and to take pleasure in life. The less pleasure and humour people find in life, the more they are liable to develop cancer. A treatment programme at the Simonton Cancer Center now specializes in helping patients to rediscover the pleasure principle, and to laugh at aspects of life they formerly found too painful to face.

All illness increases stress because it debilitates the body and because it causes fear. Stress sets in motion a complicated chain of arousal mechanisms, especially those which adversely affect the immune system. When people become seriously ill, they are under double attack, first from the illness, and second from the fear that the illness creates. So the defence system breaks down further. Therapeutic laughter could help to restore equilibrium, reduce fear and reverse the cycle of illness and debilitation.

'JOVIALISME'

In the past two years, there has been a spate of articles on laughter in a number of French magazines, which have described it as 'stationary jogging'. The recent emphasis on the importance of laughter has led to the development of '*jovialisme*' as a new movement. One of its adherents is Julie Hette, who has made a career for herself out of being a professional laugher. For a fee, she will come and laugh non-stop for you. Her record is 90 minutes. It is impossible not to be consumed with laughter oneself in her

presence, even though it is sometimes difficult to know what one is laughing about.

The new doctrine of *jovialisme* has attracted serious studies at the Sorbonne and elsewhere. Dr André Moreau, who has studied at the Sorbonne and in Montreal, Canada, believes that we should consciously seek the triggers for smiling and laughter in every aspect of our lives. Smiling and laughter open up the personality, he says, and release the positive energies that make life enjoyable and worth living.

In our present society, we are in danger of forgetting how to laugh. Studies have been undertaken on this in France, and, according to the newspaper *Le Matin*, the French population laughs less than it used to even 50 years ago. The study said that in 1930, the French laughed on average for 19 minutes a day, but in 1980, this had gone down to only six minutes a day. Asked if they would like to laugh more, 80 per cent replied with an emphatic 'yes'. More than 50 per cent of both sexes said that the ability to laugh was an important quality they sought in their sexual partners.

If it is true that we are laughing less than we used to, then it is perhaps no coincidence that stress-related diseases are on the increase. Though many previously incurable diseases have now been overcome or wiped out, we seem to be no happier than we ever were — rather the reverse, in fact.

HOSPITAL LAUGHTER ROOMS

Some doctors and lay people are now calling for more hospitals to have laughter rooms, where patients can go to see funny films, or read amusing books. It would probably not do to have the films or books available in ordinary wards, as the shrieks of patients laughing would disturb the peace and quiet sought by others. Lieutenant-Colonel Marcus McCausland, a co-founder of the charity New Approaches to Cancer, is currently setting up laughter therapy rooms for cancer patients in South Africa.

where he now lives. Now a cancer patient himself, McCausland complained to the oncology department at the Johannesburg Hospital: 'At the moment I and other patients await our turn for treatment, often for many hours, in unsuitable conditions, lined up on uncomfortable chairs in unattractive rooms.'

How much better, he wrote, if some space could be made available for a laughter room, to give relaxation, to relieve stress and to help people suffering from cancer to gain a more positive approach to their condition. 'When people are having fun and reacting amongst themselves, a very special form of attitude change occurs.'

In his outline for how laughter could best be used in cancer hospitals, McCausland suggests that a lending library of tapes, cassettes and video cassettes should be made available. Relaxation, he believes, is the best way to reverse cancer and, while this can be encouraged by good nutrition and comfortable surroundings, it is only laughter that can precipitate a change of attitude. All the good food in the world won't help while patients remain fundamentally miserable and frightened.

CONTROLLING PAIN

In his book *Natural Pain Control* Dr Vernon Coleman describes experiments where, simply by imagining pleasant rather than nasty happenings, people found their perception of pain altered.

In one experiment, Drs John Horan and John Dellinge, of Pennsylvania State University, asked 36 volunteers to place their right hands in a bucket of ice-cold water and keep them there for as long as possible. This was painful, and the volunteers withdrew their hands very quickly. They were then asked to repeat the experiment, but this time imagining pleasant, happy scenes, such as walking through a beautiful green meadow by a wonderful deep blue lake. The results were remarkable. In the first experiment, the men averaged 69 seconds in the icy water, the women 34 seconds. In the second experiment, however, the men averaged 117 seconds and the women 176 seconds.

This suggests that women may have greater powers of imagination than men, or that they respond more readily to imaginative suggestions. Dr Coleman's advice, from the results of the study, is to try and remember a joke or a funny situation next time you are in pain. 'If you imagine a situation which is inconsistent with pain, you will suffer less pain,' he claims.

According to Dr Coleman, nobody really knows how laughter and humour can have such a positive pain-relieving effect, but there is little doubt that they do. His suggestions for pain relief include collecting funny films and books, and trying to spend as much time as possible in the company of people who are happy and cheerful rather than sad. There are studies that show the importance of good company for a positive attitude of mind. 'Bright and cheerful friends will probably do you far more good than any painkilling pills the doctor can prescribe,' says Dr Coleman. He adds:

Don't take your job or life too seriously. Try to suppress pessimism and replace it with optimism. Try to start each

day in a cheerful and optimistic frame of mind. Think of things in life which are enjoyable and pleasurable. Depression and pain often make pain worse and go in a vicious circle. It can then be difficult to break out of the cycle.

Laughter expert Branko Bokun is sure that laughter, and not diamonds, is a girl's best friend. Most men, he wrote in an article on the subject for the magazine *What Diet?* would far prefer the company of a cheerful, laughing woman to one who was a perfect size 10. Moreover laughter can help you slim, as it provides such good exercise.

Alcohol is now becoming a serious problem for women, and Bokun feels sure that retaining the ability to laugh could decrease dependence on this and all other mind-altering drugs. He writes: 'Humour could eliminate the excessive use of alcohol because it helps to dissolve the problems or worries which drive us to drink in the first place.'

Scientists and doctors, at long last, are telling us what we have known intuitively for centuries, that laughter really is the best medicine, especially for stress, the cause of so many modern diseases.

6.
LAUGHTER AND FEAR

Why don't human beings smile and laugh more?
Basically, it's because we are afraid. We are afraid of life,
afraid of other people and afraid of becoming ill. The net
effect of all this worry and tension is that we become
serious, and when we are feeling serious it is very difficult
to laugh. It is also extremely difficult to laugh when afraid.
Very often, we are fearful even when there is nothing to be
nervous about. It is very easy to get into the habit of being
nervous about everything.

WHY WE BECOME ILL

What we call illness is actually a condition of disharmony
within the body and the mind. Illness happens when the
system starts breaking down. When we are in tune with
ourselves and our surroundings and at peace with the
world, we are not likely to succumb to serious illness.

Unfortunately, life is not always peaceful and
harmonious — at least not for most of us. We are
constantly beset with problems of all kinds at work, at
home, in personal relationships and in our attitude to
ourselves. Our lives may be threatened, too, by violence in
society, environmental pollution and the threat of nuclear
war. These internal and external hazards are always
there, ready to strike when defences are down, or when
resistance, for whatever reason, becomes lowered.

When we are unhappy, we are not in our rightful
element, and this in itself can affect the way the body

works. We have seen how merely simulating expressions of anger, disgust and sadness actually cause dramatic negative changes in the autonomic nervous system. The decline is bound to be much greater when we are genuinely feeling sad and miserable, rather than just pretending.

ANXIETY AND ILLNESS

Illness is not, as many doctors and medical experts like to believe, something that strikes unexpectedly out of the blue and lays low unfortunate victims through no fault of their own. Physical and mental illnesses are the result of chronic unhappiness, tension and conflict in life — conflicts that often seem impossible to resolve.

The mind plays a far larger part in determining the outcome of an illness than many people imagine. Indeed, it is not beyond the realms of possibility to suggest that the mind is primarily responsible for all bodily conditions, and that if the mind can be made well, the body has a good chance of following suit. As the poet Milton wrote in *Paradise Lost*:

> The mind is its own place and in itself
> Can make a hell of heaven, a heaven of hell.

If chronic or serious illness is to be reversed, and a state of health established, the first thing the patient must learn is how to take charge of his or her own life and to grow strong. Medical personnel can help, but they can never cure — all healing is ultimately self-healing, as Norman Cousins discovered when he applied the laughter cure. The huge doses of pain killers the doctors were prescribing him in hospital were making his condition worse, rather than better. They were taking away the perception of pain, but they were not touching the condition.

Whenever there is perpetual anxiety in a person's life, illness of some kind will eventually strike. If the anxiety is temporary or mild, the illness will be mild too. But anybody who is being torn apart by tension and worry will eventually succumb to a serious illness. Sometimes the stresses and strains in a person's life are so great that a total breakdown of health is the result.

The vast majority of illnesses can be traced back to wrong patterns of thinking, which have been allowed to become habitual and ingrained. Negative ways of thinking have the effect of damping down the body's immune system, making it more vulnerable to attack from both inside and outside. One of the greatest health destroyers of all is a constant feeling of dissatisfaction. Some people are never satisfied, but have an insatiable desire for a bigger house, a faster car or more money. They constantly want more out of life. Yet often, they do not see a corresponding need to put more into life. People who can smile and laugh are automatically giving more of themselves all the time.

When a feeling of dissatisfaction becomes chronic, depression sets in. Depression is usually considered to be a purely mental state, but its effect on the body is to deplete the immune system still further. This means that the body is at increased risk of succumbing to an illness that we may consider to be purely physical, such as a cough or cold.

Once the immune system becomes depressed, its ability to fight external viruses and internal rogue cells such as cancer becomes seriously impaired. In some very serious illnesses, such as AIDS, the immune system has packed up altogether. Cancer cells are always ready to strike, given half a chance, and are far more likely to take hold if there has been a prolonged period of unhappiness in a person's life. It is now well known that cancer commonly strikes after a bereavement or other major loss.

ANGER AND ILLNESS

Cardiovascular diseases, Britain's number one killers, tend to set in when people are living at very high pressure, and are trying to get more out of life than they are willing to put in. The result is anger, greed and all the other negative emotions that place an increased strain on the

heart and circulatory systems. It is noticeable that both
cancer and heart patients are people who have almost
always lost the ability to laugh and smile. They are so
exhausted, so nervous, so worried, that they simply
cannot laugh. Even a few minutes' laughter would help to
normalize their body functions — yet they cannot manage
it. The very idea that you can laugh at an illness and
make it go away would sound ridiculous to them, so
trapped are they in a cycle of worry and fear — of their
own making.

All of us are liable to develop unharmonious patterns of
behaviour and all of us suffer from illness at some time or
other. Nobody is immune. We are born into an imperfect
world, and as we grow up and become aware of external
realities, we may well start to respond ourselves in
negative ways, with anger, greed and misery. Instead of
developing internal strengths to help us to cope with the
ridiculous, unjust and cruel things we see around us, we
tend to allow adverse circumstances to rule our lives, and
become influenced by other people's negative thoughts
and actions.

To give a simple example — most of us react with anger
when traffic lights persist in turning against us, or when

trains are late or grind to a halt for no apparent reason. We know perfectly well that all the anger in the world will not turn the traffic lights green, nor make the train start up again, but we can't help being angry. If, instead of getting worked up at something completely beyond our control, we could laugh at these minor misfortunes, we would arrive at our destinations in a calmer and clearer state of mind.

Similarly, we tend to become enraged when others let us down or do not live up to our expectations. Perhaps we expect too much from other people. And if they cannot keep their word, that is their problem, not ours. Getting cross will not alter the situation; so we should learn instead to smile at other people's foibles.

FEAR AND ILLNESS

We become angry and upset when we do not understand either ourselves or other people. In time, we come to fear our own hostile reactions to things, and fear and worry intermingle until illness results. Everybody fears illness, and this fear is increased by all the advertisements for private health insurance and health cover that we see daily in the newspapers.

The fear of illness further burdens an already overburdened system. When people first become seriously ill, they are often terrified; if there is no understanding of what the illness means, of what has caused it, this fear increases all the time. Of course, there are good reasons for being afraid. Illness, by its very nature, is capricious, it can threaten our whole mode of life and very existence. When illness strikes, there will be uncertainty about the future, fear about medical treatment, about possible surgery, about finances and about the family. And whenever there is fear, the physical symptoms of the illness are liable to worsen, as fear itself obstructs the healing process.

Illness is feared because it is so widely misunderstood. Yet once people can realize exactly what their illness is about, and why it has come, the fear can start to fade. Only after fear has been overcome can true recovery begin. Once we allow ourselves to laugh at our illness, and at the state we have got ourselves into, the destructive cycle of fear can be broken, and the healing process set in motion.

Many doctors and nurses now appreciate that if a patient can become confident and relaxed, the outcome of any surgical or medical procedure will be so much the better. There is less likelihood of complications, and recovery time is speeded up. This is because tension and anxiety in themselves make demands on the body.

A positive outlook is also known to strengthen the power inherent in any medicine or surgical operation. Those who have faith that a particular treatment will do them good undoubtedly benefit from it. This is the well-known placebo effect, which until recently was regarded as completely unimportant. The body will very often do what the mind tells it to. The body is the car and the mind is the driver, pushing the body in one direction or another, or causing it to stall and stop. Virtually all illness starts in the mind, and so does all healing.

Since nervousness of any kind invites illness, it is essential to be able to let go of fear. Those who go through life with a fearful attitude are constantly prone to illness. Fear can actually cause certain parts of the body to become 'frozen', so that supplies of blood, hormones and nutrients no longer reach them. Laughter helps these parts to 'defrost' and to start working properly again.

A deep-seated chronic fear connected with any particular part of the body affects the flow of blood to that area. Women who suffer from gynaecological problems may be afraid of sex, afraid of unwanted pregnancy, or just not very confident about themselves as women. In a very real way, the mind cuts off a part of the body it has decided it can't cope with. When blood supply decreases, the organ in question starts to shrink up and becomes more vulnerable to infection from outside, or develops rogue cells from inside. It cannot function effectively without its proper blood supply.

Long-held fears that may have developed in childhood can often result in bad breathing habits. Many people are actually afraid of breathing properly, and this means the lungs cannot do their job. Furthermore, many years of bad breathing can set up distortions in the chemical constituents of the blood, which in time can affect the whole functioning of the body. This is a dramatic example of how fears can ultimately affect the workings of the entire body, when breathing becomes chronically shallow. Deep breathing, which is associated with relaxation and calmness, is one of the many positive side-effects of laughter. You cannot laugh and breathe shallowly at the same time.

When there is extreme fear in the mind, the heart responds by gearing itself up to prepare for an attack. If there is an opportunity to escape from the fearful situation, the heart beats faster to facilitate flight. When there is no chance of escape from the fears of the mind, the system can be geared up all the time for an attack that is never going to take place. People who go around in a perpetual agony of fear, even though there appears to be

nothing to be afraid of, are liable to have excess adrenaline pumping round their bodies all the time. When this happens, the body may eventually declare a state of emergency, and force a rest by succumbing to illness.

The longer and more serious the stress, the more severe the illness is likely to be. Our bodies respond to emotional stress in exactly the same way they would to an actual physical threat. In fact, the autonomic nervous system, which controls the output of adrenaline, does not distinguish between them.

Almost all increased stress is caused by fear. It is only when fears of all kinds — which are in reality a useless burden — can be overcome, that illness ceases to be a threat and a worry. Fears can be diminished by facing up to what is causing them, and laughter is one of the best ways of doing this. Laughter and smiling are, above all, ways of coping with problems and helping us get through life. The fears we have are not natural and inviolable, but learned behaviour, which can and should be unlearned. We don't have to practise esoteric techniques or pay for expensive courses of relaxation, but simply learn to laugh more. Gradually, the fears will recede, and in time will vanish completely. Laughter is the most potent weapon for banishing fear.

LEARNING TO RELAX

Ursula Fleming is a therapist who helps patients recover from illness by learning to relax and let go of fears. She has a story that illustrates the point:

> One cancer patient in the hospital where I work was terminally ill and there was no hope for him. He was terrified of dying, so much so that he was having a bad effect on the other patients. He was aggressive and hostile, and never laughed. I was told before I saw him that he would be aggressive towards me, and that I shouldn't expect much from him.
>
> He spent a lot of time crying and sobbing and turning his face to the wall. When I approached him he said, 'What have

you got to offer?' and intimated that he didn't believe my relaxation method could possibly do him any good. There was no way of making him laugh, as he was too far gone for that, but I asked him to listen to my music tapes at least. I saw them as a diversionary tactic, something to get his mind off his suffering. It was his fear, not his actual illness, which was making him behave so badly.

Most of my tapes are music to help patients relax. This chap said he wasn't musical, so I gave him some Mozart. Often people who say they are not musical do respond to Mozart. Gradually, he began to relax. Once it was apparent that his fears were receding, I gave him some funny music on tape and he liked that. At the same time, I was teaching him physical relaxation. Not long after, his mood improved, and he was able to smile and laugh. There was still no hope of survival but he became lighthearted, and no longer upset the other patients.

I'm convinced that, whenever there is serious illness, you have to have comic relief. There's a school of thought which says you shouldn't laugh at cancer, but really, what else can you do with it? Unless you can laugh, the whole thing becomes too burdensome for everybody, including the patient. The nurses in the unit where I work realize how important it is to have comic relief, and a great deal of laughter goes on in the cancer ward. It is essential to lighten the atmosphere, otherwise gloom and despair spreads.

Ursula also believes in the value of laughter in her relaxation classes, which are held for people suffering from severe stress as well as physical illnesses.

Whenever laughter doesn't come naturally, I induce it. At my classes, everybody has to walk in a straight line balancing a stick on their finger. Of course, nobody can do it and they keep crashing into each other. When they do this, I play funny music. It is guaranteed to break the ice and stop the classes from being too 'holy' and serious.

It's always important to stop the classes from being overserious, because this actually adds to the stress and discomfort that people feel. It's vital, though, that nobody ever laughs at anyone else.

Laughter is essential to getting well. Each of us has to understand that life has to be laughed at, otherwise it becomes unbearable. I always like that saying, 'God laughs at the wise man and the wise man laughs back.' The therapeutic effect of laughter is something that goes beyond logic, justice and all the heavy things in life. Laughter helps you to get to the truth, which is that, in the end, nothing matters all that much.

People who are afraid cannot laugh, but once they have learned to laugh, they have then triumphed over themselves and their disease. If you are going to be stuck in hospital, you might as well do whatever you can to cheer up yourself and those around you. Being miserable isn't going to shorten your stay, and it could well lengthen it. You might as well enjoy things, whatever they are. It's easier to do this once you realize the importance of laughing.

When people are unable to laugh, they are unable to relax. But, believes Ursula Fleming, relaxation in itself turns negative emotions into positive ones.

People are often asked to use willpower against fear. But this is impossible. If you exercise willpower, this means you are just sitting on your fear and keeping it there, rather than letting it go away. We now know that physical organs, such as the lining of the stomach, actually change their condition according to the emotions. Stomach linings can become literally red with anger.

The most important aspect of getting well is not so much to take the pills, or do what the doctor ordered, it's to alter the emotions. Only by changing the way you feel can you start to get better. The body responds to positive emotions, and particularly to lightheartedness.

Very often, old songs contain wisdom which could be of help to people who are afraid or ill. Here is one:

Whenever I feel afraid, I whistle a happy tune
And strike a careless pose
And no-one ever knows I'm afraid.
The cause of this deception
Is very strange to tell,
For when I fool the big bad wolf
I fool myself as well.

The biggest, baddest wolf is that which is inside the head. It is there that all fear starts, and there that all fear can end. And smiles and laughter are the best way of cutting it down to size.

7.
HOW TO HAVE A BRILLIANT SMILE

Small children smile and laugh a lot. One of the most endearing aspects of all young children is the way they throw their heads back and laugh unreservedly, taking sheer delight in the moment. As childhood advances, we tend to smile less and less until at adolescence a scowl is often the most characteristic expression. Very many teenagers hate smiling and attempt not to laugh when jokes are being made. All of a sudden it becomes 'uncool' to smile, and essential to present instead a stern, expressionless face to the world. The ability to smile and laugh spontaneously often dies during adolescence and in some people it never returns.

Teenagers don't flash ready smiles because they want to be taken seriously and feel that if they do smile, they will be treated as children. Unfortunately, losing the ability to smile can often make people miserable inside, as the personality starts to conform to the predominant facial expression.

PERFECT TEETH?

A person with a beautiful smile lights up the world and can, for that moment, make it a better place. Everybody looks more attractive when they smile, and this attractiveness is not just a matter of having dazzling white, even teeth, though these certainly do help, as studies have shown.

A large-scale study undertaken by Professor William Shaw, of the Orthodontics Department at Manchester University Dental School, showed that children were perceived as being more attractive and more intelligent when they had even, straight teeth. For the study, Professor Shaw took pictures of a series of attractive children and then superimposed pictures of crooked, missing or snaggled teeth on their faces. In all cases, the children with their own teeth were judged to be better looking, more desirable as friends, and less likely to behave aggressively than those with superimposed ugly or misshapen teeth. So teeth do matter, and those with ugly teeth may feel self-conscious about smiling.

In their book *The Dental Facelift*, American dentists Melvin and Elaine Denholtz describe the outstanding characteristics of an attractive smile.

Your smile is the most conspicuous and outstanding feature of your face. True, your eyes can be expressive, but your mouth can convey a myriad of expressions that expose your personality and emotions at any given moment. Is your mouth set in a frown or friendly grin? A grimace or an approving grin? Does your mouth transmit a cold repulse or a warm welcome? Does it express melancholy or cheerfulness?

A plain and quite ordinary face can be illuminated by a bright, open mouth that smiles. And an angry-looking face is

111

even more frightening when the mouth is turned down hard over tightly clenched teeth. Even a tired, worn, elderly face becomes beautiful when the mouth turns up into a youthful smile that communicates warmth and vitality. Why? Because your smile is the single most important punctuation mark on your face.

To assess your smile, the Denholtzes ask you to stand in front of a mirror and practise a variety of expressions, including smiling and frowning. Notice, they say, how the face immediately appears younger, livelier, more attractive, even though none of your other features have changed at all. Each person's smile is completely individual. Some smiles may be sexy and provocative, some wry, some avuncular, while others will seem fashionable and elegant. Everybody's smile says something different, but all smiles have one thing in common, and that is that they say something positive. A person who smiles exudes warmth and friendliness.

The Denholtzes give a run-down of what they consider a physically attractive smile; most of the upper teeth should show, at least two-thirds of the length, and just the tips of the lower teeth should be visible, otherwise a smile may appear too toothy. An unattractive smile, according to their definition, is one where very few teeth are visible. This type of smile, they say, can add years to your appearance, making you look far older than you really are.

COSMETIC DENTISTRY

Those who feel self-conscious about the condition of their teeth may consider cosmetic dentistry. Very often cosmetic dentistry can have a positive effect on your personality, simply because having good teeth makes you smile more and feel so much happier. Many people who have udergone extensive cosmetic dentistry say that it has quite literally changed their lives. A few years ago there was a personal account in the magazine *Cosmopolitan* by journalist Joan Burnie, who spent about £3,000 on having

a completely new set of teeth. The results were dramatic.
Her smile became far more confident and she felt
infinitely more attractive. The before-and-after pictures in
the magazine were astonishing.

Melvin and Elaine Denholtz ask in their book whether
the condition of your teeth is actually stopping you from
having the kind of smile that you would like. If you
answer 'yes' to the following questions, they say, you may
well be a candidate for cosmetic treatment. Are you
troubled and unhappy with your smile? When you smile,
do you often hold your hand near your mouth to obscure
your teeth? Are you convinced nothing can be done to
improve your smile? If so, never despair, it can.

The Denholtzes are naturally keen to promote cosmetic
dentistry as Melvin is a dentist himself and wants to sell
his services. But in the course of their book they quote
much US research which suggests that people who do not
smile readily, or whose smile is less attractive than it
could be, are perceived as less likeable than those who
smile a lot:

> Whether we like it or not, we are judged on how we appear in
> person. Job applicants are not hired on the telephone. They
> must appear for a face to face interview ... The first
> impression we make on others is hard to erase ... Who is
> more likely to get a position as a receptionist? Will it be the
> young, well-dressed applicant with a flashing smile, or the
> unkempt applicant who does not look the interviewer straight
> in the eyes?
>
> You cannot blame your teeth for every hang-up and
> personality trait you have. You cannot attribute a state of
> depression solely to your buck teeth. You cannot blame those
> gaps between your teeth for your severe anxiety. And clearly,
> your crooked teeth are not solely responsible for your lost
> career opportunities. However, there is more than a casual
> relationship between your teeth and your overall wellbeing.

In order to consider cosmetic dentistry in the first
place, you have to feel that your appearance is worth
improving. But having said that, there is no doubt that
having a beautiful smile really starts from the inside, not

from the outside. Although crooked teeth may make some people nervous of smiling, there is more to looking happy than displaying a perfect row of pearly whites. When you are genuinely pleased to see somebody, your face lights up and your eyes sparkle. This happens whatever the condition of your teeth, and is the real secret of attractiveness.

WHEN SMILING IS ESSENTIAL

There are certain occasions which always, always call for a smile. When being introduced to somebody; when trying to sell somebody something; when greeting a friend or relative; and when being interviewed. Smiles should, ideally, flash on and off. A fixed smile can give a rather robotic expression, and make the person look inane.

A false smile, as defined earlier, is one that is held just that bit too long. What you should aim for is a real smile. If your smiles are obviously false, others start to wonder what your game is and whether you are to be trusted. J.R.'s smile in the TV series *Dallas* is a prime example of a false smile. It immediately tells the viewers, though

surprisingly not always the other characters in the drama, that he is up to something dastardly again.

Happy occasions, or those which should be happy, call for brilliant, flashing smiles. As a general rule, women smile far more readily than men. In fact, experts in assertiveness training for women complain that women often smile far too much and too readily. They are more liable to want to appease others than to assert themselves. 'Women often say no, or refuse a request with a smile,' says psychologist Anne Dickson, an assertiveness expert. 'This gives the impression that they don't really mean what they say. Though the sound they make says no, their expression may actually say yes.'

Sometimes, it is true, smiles can mislead. They can be a means of softening a potentially fraught situation. Anne Dickson also feels that some women smile too much because, above all, they want to be liked and approved of. The idea is not to become a non-smiler, but to look serious when saying no, and then smile at the person afterwards, so that the smile is not taken as part of the reaction to the request. This tells the other person you mean what you say, but that you don't hate them, or think any less of them for refusing their request, nor that you expect them to think any less of you.

Men should practise smiling more. The stiff-upper-lip type of training is not conducive to health, happiness or coming closer to people. Men do not lose their dignity or position when they smile but appear more confident and at ease.

A PLEASANT LAUGH

People worry a lot about their smiles, and they also worry about how they laugh. The raucous giggle of a female teenager is not attractive, but then it is not really a laugh. It is more of a shriek, and not intended to convey any feeling of happiness. It is, rather, a sound which says 'we are all girls together'. Those not in the giggly group are excluded from the chumminess.

Actors learn to laugh to order and may spend many hours perfecting a realistic-sounding laugh for a particular part. It is noticeable that actors and actresses often live to a ripe old age, especially if they are successful, and many continue performing into their 80s and 90s. One cannot help wondering whether their ability to turn on smiles and laughter is a factor in their longevity. The connection may not be as tenuous as all that. As the old song has it: 'There's no people like show people, they smile when they are low.' Perhaps we would all be better if we could learn to be more like show people, and laugh through adversity.

A low, velvety laugh is the most attractive kind, and far nicer to listen to than a high-pitched squeak. If you hate squeals and shrieks in other people, decide to edit them out of your own laughter. You'll be surprised how easy it is. Most voice experts suggest listening to yourself on a tape recorder. Of course, not all laughter can be controlled and altered, as the essence of a belly laugh is that it *is* uncontrolled. But the more you practise laughing, and the more you listen to yourself, the easier you will find it to develop an attractive laugh. Try not to let it be too raucous — men often fall into this trap — and try also not to laugh too loudly.

A golden rule with laughter is always to laugh *with* people and never *at* them. Laughing at somebody has nothing to do with happiness or taking pleasure, but is simply a desire to appear superior. Laughing with people does not, however, need to be taken to extremes. There is no need to laugh at jokes you do not consider funny. If the joke is simply not amusing, a polite smile will do.

Sometimes people have to judge you on your voice rather than on your appearance if, for example, the only contact is by telephone. Here, American beauty expert Oleda Baker has some advice. In her book *How to Renovate Yourself From Top to Toe*, she says you should always speak with a smile on your face when answering the telephone.

> Remember that when you are on the phone you are talking to a person, not a machine. The phone is simply the medium that is bringing the two of you together. Let the tone of your voice show it ... You're not visible, either. The person on the other end of the wire cannot see your smile, the twinkle in your eye. Put them into your voice — and your vocabulary ... always answer the phone as though you expected good news. Let your voice add an exclamation mark after Hello. Too many people pick up the phone and sound bored, suspicious, sometimes downright hostile. That's such a put-off. Instead, put a smile on your face and in your voice.

There's no secret to having a brilliant smile, except to remember to smile as often as you can. The more you smile, the more you will be known for your smile, and the more popular and likeable you will become. But the real bonus is that you will gradually become happier inside at the same time.

8.
SOME FAMOUS SMILES ANALYSED

There are, as we have seen, very many different types of smile. As well as the three main varieties described by Paul Ekman — felt, false and miserable smiles — there is a very wide range which can be used to convey a multitude of feelings, nuances of feeling and moods. Smiles vary from a slight upturning of the lips to a broad grin. Generally, the happier the person, the wider and more genuine the smile.

But what about famous smiles? How do the smiles of those who are in the public eye give their owners away? The most famous smile of all time, that of the Mona Lisa in Leonardo da Vinci's painting, is hardly there at all. It is usually described as 'enigmatic', which means that the expression gives very little away. Smiles in fact seldom feature in paintings, possibly because artists have always found it difficult to portray people with genuine smiles. Apart from that, it is difficult to hold a smile, or any type of facial expression, for more than a few seconds. When held for any length of time, a smile becomes fixed and false.

For those whose face is the greatest part of their fortune, a smile is particularly important. The right kind of smile can make or mar a Hollywood star. Marilyn Monroe's smile is the apotheosis of cheesecake. It is one where the mouth is wide open and the teeth are displayed. The smile is sexually provocative, but it is a professional, 'false' smile. It is noticeable in the photographs of Marilyn Monroe that, although her mouth is showing a smile, her face as a whole does not look happy.

Farrah Fawcett has now become a serious actress and so smiles less than she used to in her *Charlie's Angels* days, when her smile was one of the most famous around. The poster featuring Farrah's toothy smile was among the best-sellers of the '70s. Whereas Marilyn Monroe's smile was obviously put on and not felt, Farrah projected an image of the natural, healthy, outdoor girl. Her teeth are large and extremely white, her gums show and the mouth is open and inviting. As Marilyn Monroe summed up the '50s, so Farrah Fawcett's smile summed up the attitudes of the '70s. Her smile is not unsexy, but is more confident and sure of itself than Marilyn's over-wide grin.

The former first lady of America, Jackie Kennedy Onassis, often has a smile which does not show her teeth. In contrast to the film-star type of smile, Jackie Onassis's is elegant and controlled. It is, again, a professional type of smile, which she wears as an accessory. It gives little of her character away.

Over the years Mrs Thatcher has perfected a professional smile. This has become more confident as her power has increased until now it is bestowed on all in the manner of Lady Bountiful. Mrs Thatcher smiles far more than she used to, and understands the value of cosmetic dentistry. Pictures of her in the early days show her with uneven teeth, but now she has a white, even smile which makes her look far more in control of all she surveys.

President Reagan, too, has a ready smile. He probably learned the importance of smiling when he was an actor, and this has stood him in good stead over the years. Reagan, unlike many politicians, is not afraid to flash a smile on and off whenever the occasion appears to demand it. Like Mrs Thatcher's, Reagan's smile is not exactly a friendly one, but tells you that he is in charge, not an underling.

One of the reasons both the Duchess of York and Princess Diana have achieved such instant, world-wide popularity is that both girls have very attractive, ready smiles. Feature for feature, Princess Diana may be more beautiful than Fergie, but Fergie's smile shows her to be a good sport. She is not shy but fun-loving, and this shows in her wide open smile which displays her bottom teeth as well as her top ones. It is noticeable that Princess Diana's smile has become far less shy than it was. Whereas she used to lower her eyes and turn her face away when smiling, she now smiles head on, and looks at the people to whom she flashes her smile. Whatever hairstyle and dresses these young Royals have, it is the 'smile' for which they are most valued.

Prince Charles finds it more difficult than his wife to smile, and has developed a rather lopsided grin. This has come about because he is essentially shy and withdrawn, but knows that his public image demands a friendly smile. Prince Andrew, more of an extrovert, has an enormous grin which displays an outstanding row of white, even teeth.

The Queen has developed a professional smile which she can flash on and off. Not a particularly outgoing or extrovert personality, the Queen has had to learn her smile. In repose, her face often looks glum and elderly, but she has retained a young-looking smile.

Among politicians, it seems that the better-looking they are, the more likely they are to smile. (Or could it be that their smiles make them better looking?) French president François Mitterrand used to have an unappealing, fanged smile which made him look rather sinister. He then had his fangs filed down — and his popularity increased as a result. Communist leaders are not noted for their ready smiles, and Brezhnev and Kruschev hardly ever seemed to smile. The present leader, Mikhail Gorbachev, looks grim when he is not smiling, but his whole face lights up when he flashes his open smile. His wife, Raisa, has a lovely smile, which may be why she is the only Russian politician's wife we have ever heard of. Nancy Reagan on the other hand, has a typical American professional smile, which has little to do with whether she is feeling happy inside. She can flash her smile on and off to order.

Personalities in the public eye are often distinguished more by their smiles than anything else. There is no doubt that a large part of singer Tina Turner's appeal lies in her

enormous open smile, which lights up her whole face. It is a professional smile, yet she manages to make it look sincere. Terry Wogan, the chat show host, has a similar ability to make his smile look real. Bob Monkhouse, another chat and game show host, long ago learned the importance of the ever-ready smile.

Female newscasters are often chosen as much for their ability to smile as for the way they read the news. The first British female newscasters, Anna Ford and Angela Rippon, became famous for their smiles rather than anything else. The present generation of newsreaders is also expected to be able to smile attractively. Male newscasters smile far less readily, and a slight, almost wry smile is considered to be enough from them.

The personalities we remember most easily are those who have learned the value of smile power — and how to use it to their advantage. A smile is like a beacon — it attracts people to you. It is noticeable that the personalities who have learned to smile tend to stay healthy and remain active for longer. Perennial stars such as Elizabeth Taylor and Sophia Loren look, if anything, more attractive as the years go by. Their smiles are one

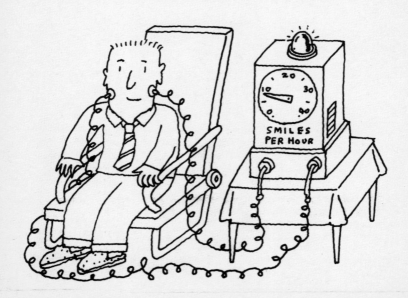

reason for this. Whatever vicissitudes they may be experiencing in their private lives, in public, at least, they have learned to keep on smiling.

Those who have learned to smile have learned the secret of a long and happy life. Those of us who find it difficult to smile when life gets tough could do well to remember the fact that smiling actually does make things better. It doesn't alter circumstances, of course, but it can alter your attitude towards circumstances — and that can make you see a better solution than when consumed with misery and self-doubt.

Many famous people are famous because they have learned to smile. Smiling makes us all that bit more memorable — so it's worth trying. Life won't get worse if you smile, and it may improve!

REFERENCES

Introduction
   The Happy Hypocrite from *The Bodley Head Beerbohm*,
   edited and introduced by David Cecil, Bodley Head, 1970.

1. What is smiling?
Ekman, Dr Paul (ed.), *Studies in Emotion and Social
   Intervention*, Cambridge University Press, 1982.
Ekman, Paul and Friesen, Wallace V., 'Felt, False and
   Miserable Smiles', *Journal of Non-Verbal Behaviour*, summer
   1982.
Ekman, Paul and Friesen, Wallace V., *Unmasking the Face*,
   Prentice Hall, 1975.
White, Dr, Burton L., *The First Three Years of Life; A Detailed
   Guide to the Physical, Emotional and Mental Development of
   Young Children*, W.H. Allen, 1978.
Hinde, Robert A. (ed.), *Non-Verbal Communication*, Cambridge
   University Press, 1972.
Pease, Allan, *Body Language*, Sheldon Press, 1981.

2. What is laughter?
Gould, Rowland, 'French Without Tears', *Best of Health*,
   January 1986.
Murdoch, Iris, *The Good Apprentice*, Penguin, 1986.

3. Having a sense of humour
Bokun, Branko, *Humour Therapy*, Vita Books, 1986.
Freud, Sigmund, *Jokes and Their Relation to the Unconscious*,
   trans. James Strachey, Routledge & Kegan Paul, 1960.
Keats, John, *You Might as Well Live: The Life and Times of
   Dorothy Parker*, Penguin, 1975.
What Rugby Jokes Did Next, Sphere Books, 1985.

4. Smile therapy: how it works
Zajonc, Robert A., *Emotional and Facial Efference: A Theory
   Reclaimed*, American Association for the Advancement of
   Science, 1985.
Ekman, Levenson, Friesen, 'Autonomic Nervous System
   Activity Distinguishes Among Emotions', *Science*, 16
   September 1983.

Ekman, P. and Scherer, K. (eds), *Expression and the Nature of Emotion*, Erlbaum, 1984.

Schmeck, Harold M., 'Say Cheese and at once you'll feel like a Junket', *New York Times*, 1983.

5. Why laughter is the best medicine

Cousins, Norman, *Anatomy of an Illness As Perceived by the Patient*, W.W. Norton and Company, 1979.

Inglis, Brian, *The Diseases of Civilization*, Hodder and Stoughton, 1981.

Dixon, Bernard, *Beyond the Magic Bullet*, Allen and Unwin, 1978.

Kittermaster, A.R., 'The Sixth Sense of Danger', *The Practitioner*, January 1983.

Coleman, Dr Vernon, *Natural Pain Control*, Century Arrow, 1986.

Bokun, Branko, 'Laughter, Woman's Best Friend', *What Diet and Lifestyle*, November/December 1986.

Gomez, Dr Joan, in *Good Health* magazine, August/September 1986.

6. Laughter and fear

Pelletier, Dr Kenneth, *Mind as Healer, Mind as Slayer*, George Allen & Unwin, 1978.

Smith, Dr Trevor, *Emotional Health*, Insight Editions, 1986.

Kidman, Brenda, *A Gentle Way with Cancer*, Century, 1983.

Werthman, Michael, *Self-Psyching*, Bachman and Turner, 1978.

Brohn, Penny, *Gentle Giants*, Century, 1986.

7. How to have a brilliant smile

Denholtz, Melvin and Denholtz, Elaine, *The Dental Facelift*, Van Nostrand Reinhold, 1981.

Baker, Oleda, *How to Renovate Yourself from Head to Toe*, Futura, 1982.

Shaw, W.C., Rees, G., Dawe, M., and Charles, C.R., 'The Influence of Dentofacial Appearance on the Social Attractiveness of Young Adults', *American Journal of Orthodontics*, January 1985.

Shaw, W.C., and Humphreys, S., 'Influence of Children's Dentofacial Appearance on Teacher Expectations', *Social Psychology*, 1982.

ABOUT THE AUTHOR

LIZ HODGKINSON is a freelance journalist and author specializing in health and related topics.

To date she has written seven books, and has contributed to most national newspapers and magazines. Her book, *Sex is Not Compulsory* (published in 1986), attracted world-wide public interest by querying established ideas about our sexual needs, both emotional and physical.

Herself a feminist and a vegetarian, Liz Hodgkinson is interested in living a healthy, independent, autonomous lifestyle, and feels that smiling is an essential part of this.

She is married, with two grown-up sons, and lives in Richmond, Surrey.